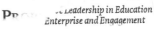

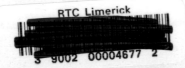

PROBLEMS

IN

PHYSICAL ORGANIC CHEMISTRY

Anthony R. Butler

University of St. Andrews

JOHN WILEY & SONS

London · New York · Sydney · Toronto

Library of Congress catalog card number 72–617

ISBN 0 471 12680 2

Printed in Great Britain by J. W. Arrowsmith Ltd., Bristol 3

Preface

Physical organic chemistry is a subject of increasing research activity and this activity is reflected in the way that organic chemistry is taught. A study of the use of physical measurements in elucidating reaction mechanisms is an important part of any advanced course in organic chemistry, and such a study is well suited to instruction by the discussion of examples from the chemical literature. This method has been used for a number of years with undergraduates at the University of St. Andrews, and it is hoped that the examples used will be of value to other students of the subject.

Thanks must be given to many investigators all over the world who have provided so much illuminating and instructive material. I would like to take this opportunity of thanking Mr. H. R. Hore, who did so much to stimulate my interest while at school, Professor Lord Tedder for reading the manuscript and writing a foreword, and finally Miss Helen Wallace, who carefully checked each problem and made many valuable suggestions. The remaining errors and omissions are the sole responsibility of the author.

October, 1971

Anthony R. Butler
St. Andrews

Foreword

An understanding of physical science can only be achieved by participating. Learning by note may enable a student to acquire an assembly of facts and laws but comprehension cannot be attained this way. Full participation can only be achieved by taking part in research and the nearer the student can be brought to problems confronting the research worker the fuller will be his understanding of the subject. In the present book, Dr. Butler, himself an active researcher in the field of Physical Organic Chemistry, has brought together a collection of problems in this field. The problems are of graded difficulty the more advanced being taken directly from the research literature. A student who works through this book will indeed have participated and will have gained an understanding of this important branch of Organic Chemistry. A straight reading of problem and answer will prove a valuable exercise though it is hoped that most readers will seek to complete their own answer before comparing it with the one provided. This book will help not only students but active workers who will I am sure find their ideas clarified, as I did.

Tedder

Introduction

This book of problems is intended as an aid to students taking courses in physical organic chemistry. As the solutions to the problems are given, the book is not suitable for seminars or tutorials, although some questions have been left partly 'open-ended' to permit their use in discussion. The first part of the book is a series of straight forward exercises on specific topics and each section is preceded by a short discussion, with references to the literature of the subject. In using the problems it is suggested that the student covers the solution with a sheet of paper, works through the problem, and then checks his answer against that given. Nearly all the problems are taken from original research papers and should any aspect of the problem interest or puzzle the student, he can take recourse to the original paper for further information and discussion.

The second part of the book is a collection of more general problems involving several topics coming within the general field of physical organic chemistry, and may be found useful by students preparing for examinations involving 'problem' papers or at the conclusion of a course of lectures. This part of the book should be used in the same way as the first. Problems which may be found difficult, or involve considerable calculation, are indicated by an asterisk.

Undergraduates rarely have occasion to consult research papers during their studies and this is a serious omission. In several exercises, therefore, such consultation is necessary before the problem can be solved. This has the disadvantage of making the problem more time consuming and has been used sparingly.

The main difficulty experienced in preparing this collection of problems has been defining the term 'physical organic chemistry'. There are already several collections of problems on structure determination, and also spectroscopy, and these topics have not been included. What topics are rightly called 'physical organic' is, in the final analysis, a matter of the author's choice but it is hoped that the student will not find the scope too limited to be of value. During the preparation of this book the second edition of Hammett's *Physical Organic Chemistry* appeared and, broadly, the topics discussed there have been included in this present volume. As Professor Hammett did so much to initiate study of the subject, it is not unreasonable to use his text as definitive. In general, the problems permit the elucidation of a reaction mechanism by the use of quantitative data.

Contents

Part 1

The Literature of Physical Organic Chemistry

It is impossible to mention all the books which might be included under this heading but the following are amongst those most commonly in use. In this collection of problems they will be referred to by the names of the authors. More specialized texts, and review articles, will be mentioned in the appropriate places.

R. W. Alder, R. Baker, and John M. Brown, *Mechanism in Organic Chemistry*, Wiley-Interscience, London, 1971. R. P. Bell, *Acid–Base Catalysis*, Oxford University Press, Oxford, 1941. E. S. Gould, *Mechanism and Structure in Organic Chemistry*, Holt, Rinehard, and Winston, New York, 1959. L. P. Hammett, *Physical Organic Chemistry*, 2nd ed., McGraw-Hill, New York, 1970. J. Hine, *Physical Organic Chemistry*, 2nd ed., McGraw-Hill, New York, 1962. C. K. Ingold, *Structure and Mechanism in Organic Chemistry*, 2nd ed., G. Bell, London, 1970. E. M. Kosower, *An Introduction to Physical Organic Chemistry*, Wiley, New York, 1968. J. E. Leffler and E. Grunwald, *Rates and Equilibria of Organic Reactions*, Wiley, New York, 1963. K. B. Wiberg, *Physical Organic Chemistry*, Wiley, New York, 1964.

Inductive, Resonance, and Steric Effects

These topics are discussed in all the texts on physical organic chemistry and, indeed, in most books on organic chemistry. In view of the monumental contribution made to the study of these effects upon chemical reactivity, Ingold's book must remain the source book for subsequent reviews but it may be too detailed for most undergraduate courses. The *I, T,* and *M* nomenclature of Ingold has not been adopted. A clear and descriptive terminology is that due to Tedder and Nechvatal (*Basic Organic Chemistry,* Part 2, Wiley, London, 1967) and will be used here. The inductive effect is described as 'electron-attracting' or 'electron-repelling' and the mesomeric effect as 'electron-accepting' or 'electron-donating'. There is an interesting article by G. V. Calder and T. J. Barton [*J. Chem. Ed.,* **48**, 338 (1971)] which indicates that the simple accounts given in many textbooks are not in agreement with all the experimental data.

1. Which is the stronger acid of the following pairs and why?

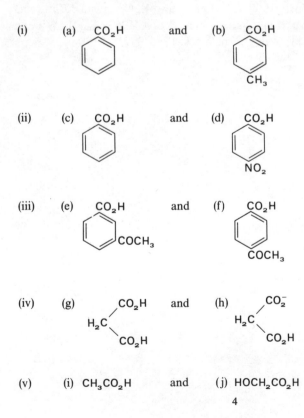

(i)   (a) CO_2H and   (b) CO_2H / CH_3

(ii)   (c) CO_2H and   (d) CO_2H / NO_2

(iii) (e) CO_2H / $COCH_3$ and   (f) CO_2H / $COCH_3$

(iv)   (g) H_2C (CO_2H)(CO_2H)   and   (h) H_2C (CO_2^-)(CO_2H)

(v)   (i) CH_3CO_2H and   (j) $HOCH_2CO_2H$

Solution. The strength of an acid depends upon the stability of the anion formed on ionization and this, in turn, depends upon the extent of delocalization of the negative charge.

(i) The methyl group is electron-repelling and (b) is weaker than (a).

(ii) The nitro group is strongly electron-accepting and (d) is stronger than (c).

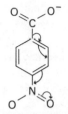

(iii) The mesomeric effect of the acetyl group is electron-accepting but this cannot be relayed from the *m*-position, so (f) is stronger than (e).

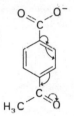

(iv) The second dissociation of malonic acid is much less than the first as it involves separation of a proton from a species which is already negatively charged so that (g) is a stronger acid than (h).

(v) The hydroxy group is electron-attracting so (j) is stronger than (i).

pK_a values for all these acids can be found in A. Albert and E. P. Serjeant, *Ionization Constants of Acids and Bases*, Methuen, London, 1962.

2. Discuss the pK_a values of the carboxylic acids given. (A lower pK_a indicates a stronger acid.)

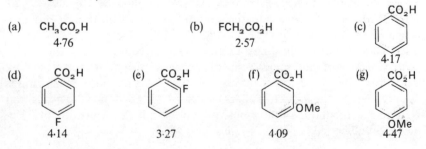

(a) CH_3CO_2H
     4·76

(b) FCH_2CO_2H
     2·57

(c) CO_2H
     4·17

(d) CO_2H
     F
     4·14

(e) CO_2H
     F
     3·27

(f) CO_2H
     OMe
     4·09

(g) CO_2H
     OMe
     4·47

Solution. Electron-attracting groups like fluoro delocalize the negative charge on the anion and so (b) is a stronger acid than (a). This is true of *p*-fluorobenzoic acid but the mesomeric effect acts in the opposite sense, so a *p*-fluoro substituent has little effect on the pK_a of benzoic acid. There may also be a further important factor known as the I_π effect: this is discussed by Tedder and Nechvatal (*Basic Organic Chemistry*, Part 2, Wiley, London, p. 70). In the *o*-position the inductive effect is increased because of the reduced distance and (e) is a stronger acid than benzoic acid. There may also be a steric factor, forcing the carboxyl group out of the plane of the ring and reducing the acid-weakening properties of the benzene ring. The inductive effect of the methoxy group is sufficient to make (f) a slightly stronger acid than benzoic. However, an electron-donating mesomeric effect can be relayed from the *p*-position and the result is that *p*-methoxybenzoic acid is weaker than benzoic acid. D. J. G. Ives and J. H. Pryor, *J. Chem. Soc.*, **1955**, 2104. J. F. J. Dippy and R. H. Lewis, *J. Chem. Soc.*, **1936**, 644.

3. Predict the distribution of isomers obtained by the electrophilic mono-chlorination of the following substances.

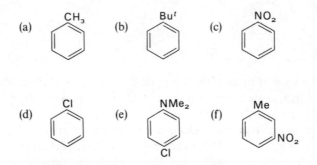

Solution. (a) The methyl group is *ortho/para* directing and gives approximately the distribution expected on statistical grounds (60 % *o* and 40 % *p*).

(b) With the *t*-butyl group the amount of *o*-substitution is reduced, probably for steric reasons (22 % *o* and 76 % *p*).

(c) The nitro group is almost exclusively *m*-directing.

(d) Chlorine donates electrons mesomerically but attracts them by induction. The former effect makes chlorine *o/p* directing but the ring is deactivated. As the inductive effect decreases with distance the *o*-position is more deactivated than the *p*-position and so a high proportion of *p*-isomer is obtained (33 % *o* and 55 % *p*).

(e) Predominant attack is at the position o to the $-NMe_2$ group, illustrating the dominance of the o/p directing properties of $-NMe_2$ over the less powerful chlorine.

(f) Attack is o and p to the methyl group showing that the effect of the methyl group (which is activating as well as o/p directing) is stronger than that of the nitro group (which is m-directing but *deactivating*).

Data for these and similar reactions can be found in P. B. D. de la Mare and J. Ridd, *Aromatic Substitution*, Butterworth, London, 1959.

4. Squaric acid ionizes directly to the dianion and is a stronger acid than sulphuric.

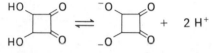

Explain these effects.

Solution. The strength of an acid depends largely upon the stability of the anion. The dianion of squaric acid is particularly stable owing to extensive

delocalization of the electrons to give a completely symmetrical dianion. G. Maahs and P. Hegenberg, *Angew. Chem. Intern. Ed. Engl.*, **5**, 888 (1966).

5. Aromatic iodination may be effected by reaction with thallium trifluoro-acetate in trifluoroacetic acid and subsequent treatment with aqueous potassium iodide, all at room temperature.

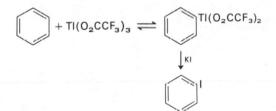

The following isomer ratios were obtained for a number of compounds:

	Isomer distribution		
	$\% o$	$\% m$	$\% p$
$PhCH_2OH$	100	0	0
$PhCH_2OCH_3$	100	0	0
$PhCH_2CH_2OCH_3$	85	3	12
$PhCH_2CH_2CH_2OH$	12	9	79
$PhCH_2CH_2CH_3$	3	6	91

In the last case, if the reaction mixture is refluxed during thallation, the isomer distribution is changed to 9% *o*, 78% *m*, and 13% *p*.

Suggest reasons for (a) exclusive *ortho* attack with benzyl alcohol and benzyl methyl ether, (b) an increase in the amount of *p*-isomer as the chain length is increased, and (c) the change to *m*-substitution on refluxing.

Solution. Exclusive *ortho* attack may be explained by complexing of thallium at a basic site in the side chain

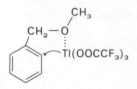

and subsequent attack at the *o*-position. As the basic site is moved further from the ring this no longer affects the site of thallation and the *p*-compound is formed. Thallation is a reversible process and, while normally kinetic factors decide the position of thallation in the absence of a side chain containing a basic site, refluxing produces the thermodynamically most stable isomer (i.e. the *m*-compound). E. C. Taylor, F. Kienzle, R. L. Robey, and A. McKillop, *J. Amer. Chem. Soc.*, **92**, 2175 (1970).

6. Two reactions frequently used in measuring the reactivity of an aromatic compound towards electrophilic attack are (a) hydrogen exchange in trifluoroacetic acid (protodetritiation), and (b) protodesilylation. Both of these have been examined with respect to the 1-position of biphenylene.

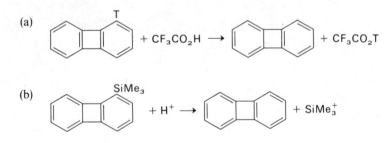

The following partial rate factors for the two reactions were obtained:

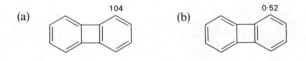

Comment on these values (consider carefully the definition of the term 'partial rate factor').

Solution. The 1-position of biphenylene is unusual in being activated (with respect to a position in benzene) towards hydrogen exchange, but *deactivated* in protodesilylation. This probably indicates that the simple picture of the ease and orientation of electrophilic substitution depending upon resonance stabilization of the Wheland intermediate is an over simplification of the situation. Activation, or deactivation, of a position depends also upon the demand for resonance stabilization of the transition state which, with biphenylene, appears to be much greater for hydrogen exchange than for protodesilylation. J. M. Blatchly and R. Taylor, *J. Chem. Soc.* (*B*), **1964**, 4641. R. Taylor, *J. Chem. Soc.* (*B*), **1971**, 536.

7. Explain the variation of partial rate factor obtained in the nitration of a series of alkylbenzenes.

	o	*m*	*p*
toluene	49·7	1·3	60·0
ethylbenzene	31·4	2·3	69·5
isopropylbenzene	14·8	2·4	71·6
t-butylbenzene	4·5	3·0	75·5

Solution. The *meta/para* ratio changes very little along the series showing that the polar effects of the alkyl groups are very similar. However, there is a dramatic decrease in the amount of *o*-substitution and this is due to steric factors. J. R. Knowles, R. O. C. Norman, and G. K. Radda, *J. Chem. Soc.*, **1960**, 4885.

8. Alkyl substitution normally increases the basicity (pK_a is larger) of pyridine but the following results were obtained for 2,6-di-*t*-butylpyridine in three different solvents.

	20% aq. methanol	20% aq. ethanol	20% aq. 2-propanol
pyridine	5·12	5·09	4·96
2-*t*-butylpyridine	5·65	5·61	5·56
2,6-di-*t*-butylpyridine	5·06	4·81	4·61

The weakening effect of the second *t*-butyl group may be due to (a) steric strain on the bound proton [H. C. Brown and B. Kanner, *J. Amer. Chem. Soc.*, **88**, 986 (1966)), or (b) steric inhibition of solvation (E. E. Condon, *J. Amer. Chem. Soc.*, **87**, 4494 (1965)].

Assuming that the effect of alkyl substituents should be additive, show which of these explanations is consistent with the above data.

Solution. The difference between the calculated pK_a, assuming that the effect of the second *t*-butyl group is the same as the first, and the experimentally determined one varies with the solvent, so favouring explanation (b). D. H. McDaniel and M. Özcan, *J. Org. Chem.*, **33**, 1922 (1968).

Hammett Relationship

The Hammett $\sigma\rho$ equation puts on a quantitative basis the effect of substituents on reaction rates covered in the previous section. The equation is discussed in all the texts on physical organic chemistry. In an interesting footnote (p. 355) Hammett provides some insight into the unique association of his name with this equation. He claims that it is somewhat undeserved and Ingold, very correctly, refers to it as the Hammett–Burkhardt equation. Whatever name is used, it is easier than calling it 'the linear free energy relationship involving *meta*- and *para*-substituted benzene derivatives'.

Hammett includes a full discussion on the modified forms of σ, as well as extensions of the original equation (e.g. Taft and Yakawa–Tsuno equations). For a full treatment of these topics it is best to consult the specialist monograph by P. R. Wells (*Linear Free Energy Relationships*, Academic Press, New York, 1968). The topic is covered comprehensively by Leffler and Grunwald. The separation of steric and polar effects has been reviewed by Shorter [*Quart. Rev. London*, **24**, 433 (1970)]. Non-linear Hammett plots are discussed in an article by J. O. Schreck [*J. Chem. Ed.*, **48**, 103 (1971)].

In these exercises only the simple Hammett equation will be used, involving σ, σ^-, and σ^+. The required values of the σ constants are given in the following table. The most complete collection is that of D. H. McDaniel and H. C. Brown [*J. Org. Chem.*, **23**, 420 (1958)].

Substituent	Hammett constants		
	σ	σ^+	σ^-
p-MeO	-0.27	-0.78	-0.27
m-MeO	0.12	0.05	
p-Me	-0.17	-0.31	-0.17
m-Me	-0.07	-0.07	-0.07
p-Bu^t	-0.20	-0.26	
m-Bu^t	-0.10	-0.06	
p-F	0.06	-0.07	
m-F	0.34	0.35	
p-Br	0.23	0.15	0.22
m-Br	0.39	0.41	
p-Cl	0.23	0.11	
m-Cl	0.37	0.40	0.38
p-CO$_2$Et	0.45	0.48	0.68
p-NO$_2$	0.78	0.79	1.27
m-NO$_2$	0.71	0.67	0.70

9. Under strongly alkaline conditions (methoxide ion) HCl is eliminated from 2-chloro-2-methyl-1-phenylpropane to give 2-methyl-1-phenylprop-1-ene.

$$\text{PhCH}_2\text{CMe}_2\text{Cl} \rightarrow \text{PhCH}{=}\text{CMe}_2 + \text{HCl}$$

From the following results for the effect of substituents in the phenyl ring on the rate of reaction, determine the Hammett value for this reaction.

Substituent	m-Cl	m-F	p-Cl	m-MeO	H	m-Me	p-MeO
Relative rate (k/k_0)	2·23	2·21	1·77	1·38	1·00	0·77	0·60

Solution. A plot of $\log(k/k_0)$ against σ is linear (as shown in Figure 1). The

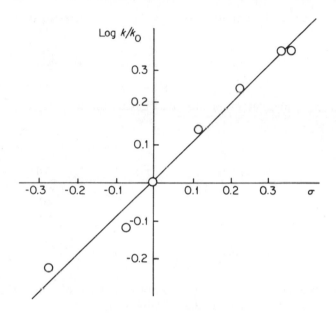

Figure 1. Plot of $\log(k/k_0)$ against σ.

slope of this line (the value of ρ) is 1·0. L. F. Blackwell, A. Fischer, and J. Vaughan, *J. Chem. Soc.* (*B*), **1967**, 1084.

10. The following partial rate factors (k_f) were obtained for the bromination of monosubstituted benzenes by hypobromous acid in 50% aqueous dioxan containing perchloric acid.

Substituent	p-Me	p-Bu^t	m-Me	m-Bu^t	H	p-Cl	p-Br
k_f	58·9	38·9	2·51	2·57	1·00	0·22	0·15

Show that the values of k_f fit a Hammett equation using σ^+ values and determine the value of ρ. Predict the k_f value for p-fluorobenzene.

Do these results allow you to distinguish between H_2^+OBr and Br^+ as the brominating species?

Solution. A plot of log k_f against σ^+ is linear and $\rho = -5.95$. The value of k_f for *p*-fluorobenzene is 2·53. The results do not permit the brominating species to be fixed.

11. The mechanism of semicarbazone formation from benzaldehyde involves condensation, followed by elimination of water.

$$\mathrm{PhCHO} + \mathrm{NH_2NHCONH_2} \underset{k_{-1}}{\overset{k_1}{\rightleftharpoons}} \overset{\displaystyle \mathrm{OH}}{\mathrm{Ph\overset{|}{C}H{-}NHNHCONH_2}}$$

$$\overset{\displaystyle \mathrm{OH}}{\mathrm{Ph\overset{|}{C}H{-}NHNHCONH_2}} \overset{k_2}{\rightarrow} \mathrm{PhCH{=}N{-}NHCONH_2} + \mathrm{H_2O}$$

The second step (k_2) is acid-catalysed. The effect of substituents in the benzene ring of benzaldehyde upon the rate of reaction depends upon the pH, as shown by the following figures.

	Relative rate	
Substituent	pH = 1·75	pH = 7·00
p-OMe	0·52	0·81
p-Me	0·54	0·90
H	1·00	1·00
p-Cl	1·14	1·15
m-NO$_2$	3·36	1·21
p-NO$_2$	4·93	1·53

Calculate the Hammett ρ value at both pH's and explain the difference in terms of a change in the rate-determining step.

Solution. At pH = 7·00 the rate-determining step is dehydration. Assuming that the intermediate is present at low steady state, the kinetic equation is the following:

$$\mathrm{Rate} = \frac{k_2 k_1}{k_{-1}}[\mathrm{PhCHO}][\mathrm{NH_2NHCONH_2}][\mathrm{H^+}]$$

Electron-donating substituents increase the rate of the acid-catalysed step (k_2) but have the opposite effect on the equilibrium (k_1/k_{-1}), so that at neutral pH the rate is not greatly affected by substitution $(\rho = 0.07)$. In acid solution (pH = 1·75) the second step is so fast (because of acid-catalysis) that it is no longer rate-determining and the slow step is k_1, making the overall reaction no longer acid-catalysed. The value of ρ at this pH (= 0·91) reflects the effect of substituents on nucleophilic attack of semicarbazide on the carbonyl group of benzaldehyde. B. M. Anderson and W. P. Jencks, *J. Amer. Chem. Soc.*, **82**, 1773 (1960).

12. Protonation of carboxylic acid may occur either on the hydroxy group or on the carbonyl oxygen to give **1** or **2**.

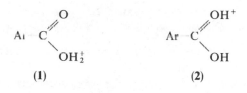

(1)   (2)

The equilibrium constants for protonation of a number of substituted benzoic acids have been determined.

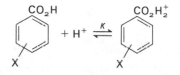

Substituent	H	m-Me	p-Me	m-MeO	p-MeO	m-Cl	p-Cl	m-NO$_2$
−pK	7·26	7·19	6·92	7·45	6·68	7·73	7·48	7·97

Consider carefully the reactions which define σ and σ^+ and, by correlation of the above results with one of these, determine the position of protonation.

Solution. If protonation occurs on the hydroxy group the positive charge cannot be delocalized in the ring, except by inductive effects. However, this is not the case for protonation on the carbonyl oxygen (**3**) and the

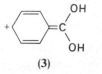

(3)

species formed in this case is very similar to that occurring in electrophilic aromatic substitution. The fact that the above figures correlate better with σ^+ than with σ indicates protonation of the carbonyl group. R. Stewart and K. Yates, *J. Amer. Chem. Soc.*, **82**, 4059 (1960).

13. The reaction between ethyl chloroformate and aniline is a two-step process, involving addition followed by elimination.

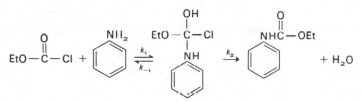

The following kinetic data were obtained for the effect of substituents in the aniline on the rate of reaction.

Substituent	p-OMe	p-Me	m-Me ·	H	p-Br	m-Cl	p-CO₂ Et	m-NO₂	p-NO₂
$10^3 k_{obs}$ l mol^{-1} sec^{-1}	1209	286	66·5	42·4	5·57	5·25	1·53	1·92	0·13

What may be deduced about the rate-determining step in this reaction from a plot of log k_{obs} against σ^-?
Suggest an experimental check on the proposed mechanism.

Solution. The Hammett plot shows a distinct break with p-OMe, p-Me, m-Me, and H on one line ($\rho = -5·5$) and the other substituents on another line ($\rho = -1·6$). This indicates a change of rate-determining step. For anilines with diminished nucleophilicity (i.e. with electron-withdrawing substituents) the slow step is the first (k_1) but, with increased nucleophilicity, this step becomes fast and k_2 is rate-controlling.

One experimental method of showing this change of rate-determining step would be to demonstrate the transient intermediate spectrophotometrically. This should only be possible in cases where k_2 is less than k_1, i.e. the slow step is decomposition of the intermediate. G. Ostrogovich, G. Csunderlik, and R. Bacaloglu, *J. Chem. Soc. (B)*, **1971**, 18.

14*. In the presence of a base (potassium *t*-butoxide in *t*-butanol) 2-phenylethylbenzene sulphonate undergoes elimination to give styrene and the mechanism of the reaction is *E*2.

$$\text{(A)}-\overset{\beta}{\text{CH}_2}\overset{\alpha}{\text{CH}_2}-\text{OSO}_2-\text{(B)} \rightarrow \text{(...)}-\text{CH}=\text{CH}_2 + \text{HOSO}_2\text{(...)}$$

A kinetic study of the effect of substituents in ring B, with the same substituent in ring A, on the rate of reaction gives a good Hammett plot with slope of ρ. Values of ρ have been determined as a function of the substituent in ring A, with the following results.

Substituent in ring A	p-OMe	p-Me	H	m-OMe	p-Cl	m-Cl
Hammett ρ value	1·24	1·24	1·08	1·06	1·01	0·94

(A more positive ρ value indicates greater accumulation of negative charge.) How does the trend in the values of ρ reflect changes in the transition state with different substituents in ring A?

Solution. The mechanism of elimination is as shown and what may vary

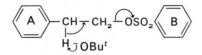

in the transition state is the extent of breaking of the C_β—H bond *or* the C_α—O bond. With a constant substituent in ring A the magnitude of ρ (which depends upon variation of substituents in ring B) reflects the amount of negative charge present on the oxygen of the sulphonate group *in the transition state*. Therefore, with *p*-OMe in ring A there is more negative charge in the sulphonate group than with *m*-Cl. These substituents will also affect the acidity of the hydrogen on the β-carbon atom, the most acidic being substituted *m*-Cl. Thus, the more the C_β—H bond is weakened in the transition state the less will be the C_α—O bond. The *p*-OMe substituent in ring A will give rise to the least carbanion-like transition state and the *m*-Cl the most. A. F. Cockerill, J. Banger, and G. L. O. Davies, *J. Chem. Soc. (B)*, **1971**, 498. [These results are in conflict with those of H. M. R. Hoffman (*Tetrahedron Letters*, **1967**, 4393) who suggests, from work on the relative rates of elimination of bromide and tosylate, that increased C_β—H bond breaking induces greater C_α—X bond breaking.]

Product Analysis

It seems almost unnecessary to suggest that product analysis should be part of any investigation into a reaction mechanism but in kinetic studies, particularly where the rate of disappearance of a reactant is being studied, this has sometimes been neglected and erroneous conclusions drawn. The following problems illustrate how identification of the main products, and detection of side products, may lead to a greater understanding of a reaction mechanism. Ion-pair formation is discussed by Alder, Baker, and Brown and by Hammett.

15. In the benzidine rearrangement of 2-ethoxy-2'-methylhydrazobenzene the *only* product is 3-ethoxy-3'-methylbenzidine.

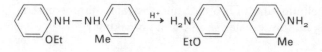

What characteristic of the benzidine rearrangement can be deduced from this?

Solution. The reaction must be *intra*molecular. If there was cleavage to two fragments of the same type, followed by recombination, three different products would result. G. W. Wheland and J. R. Schwartz, *J. Chem. Phys.*, **17**, 425 (1949).

16. In a polar solvent bromine adds to ethylene to give dibromoethane. However, in the presence of sodium chloride some 1-bromo-2-chloroethane is formed. Explain this finding.

Solution. The first step in the reaction is addition of a bromine cation to give a carbonium ion (**1**), and this may be attacked by any nucleophile (bromide or chloride) present in the solution. Probably a three-membered

$$CH_2{=}CH_2 + \overset{\delta^+}{Br}{-}\overset{\delta^-}{Br} \rightarrow \quad H_2C\overset{\overset{\displaystyle Br}{\overset{+}{\cdots}}}{\cdots}CH_2 + Br^-$$

(**1**)

$$H_2C\overset{\overset{\displaystyle Br}{\overset{+}{\cdots}}}{\cdots}CH_2{\diagdown}_{Br^-} \rightarrow CH_2Br{-}CH_2Br \quad \text{(Normal product)}$$

$$H_2C\overset{\overset{\displaystyle Br}{\overset{+}{\cdots}}}{\cdots}CH_2{\diagdown}_{Cl^-} \rightarrow CH_2Br{-}CH_2Cl$$

16

cyclic 'bromonium ion' is formed. A. W. Francis, *J. Amer. Chem. Soc.*, **47**, 2340 (1925). I. Roberts and G. E. Kimball, *J. Amer. Chem. Soc.*, **59**, 947 (1937).

17. In solution in the dark hydrogen bromide adds to allyl bromide to give 1,2-dibromopropane. In the presence of a trace of benzoyl peroxide, however, the product is 1,3-dibromopropane. Suggest a mechanism for 1,3-addition.

Solution. In the presence of benzoyl peroxide hydrogen halides add by a free-radical mechanism.

$$Peroxide \rightarrow R\cdot$$

$$R\cdot + HBr \rightarrow RH + Br\cdot$$

$$Br\cdot + CH_2{=}CHCH_2Br \rightarrow BrCH_2{-}\dot{C}HCH_2Br$$

$$BrCH_2{-}\dot{C}HCH_2Br + HBr \rightarrow BrCH_2CH_2CH_2Br + Br\cdot$$

The bromine radical (Br$\cdot$) adds to the same carbon atom as H$^+$ does in solution in the dark, so a different product is obtained. It may be that attack occurs at the site which leads to the more stable free radical but this does not appear to be the complete explanation. M. S. Kharasch, H. Engelmann, and F. R. Mayo, *J. Org. Chem.*, **2**, 288 (1937).

18. In the presence of HCl an aromatic *N*-nitrosamine rearranges to give a *C*-nitroso compound (the Fisher–Hepp rearrangement). Do the following

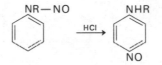

observations indicate an *inter-* or *intra*molecular rearrangement?

(a) In the presence of urea only a secondary aromatic amine is obtained.

(b) If dimethylaniline is added the main product is *p*-nitrosodimethylaniline.

(c) Nitrosyl chloride (NOCl) reacts rapidly with aromatic amines to give a *C*-nitroso compound.

Suggest a possible reaction mechanism.

Solution. All the evidence is in favour of an *inter*molecular rearrangement. Urea reacts with nitrous acid and, as no nitrosated product is obtained in the presence of urea, the nitrosating species must be separated from the *N*-nitrosamine. Cross-nitrosation in the presence of dimethylaniline leads to the same conclusion. The reaction of nitrosyl chloride suggests that this is the intermediate, formed from *N*-nitrosamine and HCl, responsible for nitrosation.

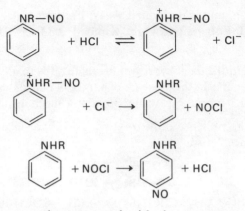

This mechanism may be compared with the rearrangement of *N*-nitro-aniline (see Problem 81). W. G. Macmillen and T. H. Reade, *J. Chem. Soc.,* **1929**, 583. B. T. Baliga, *J. Org. Chem.,* **35**, 2031 (1970).

[The situation may not be as simple as suggested above. This reaction has been investigated extensively by W. N. White and coworkers and, for further information, this work should be consulted (*J. Org. Chem.,* **35**, 2759 (1970)).]

19. In the presence of HCl *N*-chloroacetanilide rearranges to give *o*- and *p*-chloroacetanilide (the Orton rearrangement).

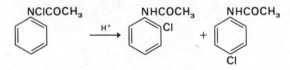

If air is bubbled through the reaction mixture it is found to contain chlorine. Suggest a mechanism for the rearrangement.

Solution. The detection of free chlorine means that the rearrangement is

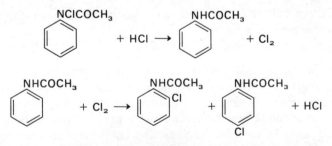

*inter*molecular and indicates the mechanism shown. K. J. P. Orton and W. J. Jones, *J. Chem. Soc.,* **95**, 1456 (1909).

20*. Bridgehead halides react with silver nitrate with replacement of the halide. In a study of the reaction of an excess of 1-adamantyl chloride with ethanolic silver nitrate the product, after complete reaction of the nitrate, was found to contain 80% 1-adamantyl nitrate and 20% 1-ethoxyadamantane. This ratio was found to be *independent* of the concentration of silver nitrate. What does this indicate about the mechanism of the reaction?

Solution. The most obvious mechanism is formation of a free 1-adamantyl carbonium ion which then reacts competitively with nitrate ion and solvent to give the two products (i.e. an S_N1 mechanism). However, this cannot be correct as raising the nitrate ion concentration should increase the proportion of nitrate formed. It suggests, instead, formation of an ion-pair containing 1-adamantyl carbonium ion and a nitrate ion. Collapse of this ion-pair leads to formation of the nitrate and separation to solvolysis of the adamantyl ion to 1-ethoxyadamantane. D. N. Kevill and V. M. Horvath, *Tetrahedron Letters*, **1971**, 711. [For a more complete discussion of ion-pair formation see G. S. Hammond, M. F. Hawthorne, J. H. Waters, and B. M. Graybill, *J. Amer. Chem. Soc.*, **82**, 704 (1960).]

Kinetics

Of all the techniques available to the physical organic chemist for the elucidation of reaction mechanism, a study of reaction kinetics is probably the
most powerful. Most texts assume a knowledge of the integrated rate
equations and few deal specifically with kinetics, although Gould has a
chapter on kinetic methods of determining reaction mechanism, but make
frequent use of the results of kinetic studies. Most advanced texts on kinetics
treat the subject more from the point of view of a physical chemist. A. A. Frost
and R. G. Pearson, *Kinetics and Mechanism* (Wiley, New York, 1961) is the
most useful source of information for organic chemists and gives the inte-
gration of most of the rate equations commonly encountered. A recent
review by R. Huisgen [*Angew. Chem. Intern. Ed. Engl.*, **9**, 751 (1970)] deals
specifically with the use of kinetic studies for the detection of reaction intermediates. Wiberg gives computer programmes for some integrated rate
equations.

Many problems involving kinetic studies will be found in Part 2 of this
collection, but a few straightforward examples are given below. Calculation
of rate constants from kinetic data is a time-consuming task so in all cases
the student is presented with them precalculated.

21. In most instances hydrolysis of an alkyl halide is catalysed by hydroxide
ion. However, the rate of hydrolysis of t-butyl chloride in aqueous ethanol
is almost unaffected by addition of potassium hydroxide. Suggest a reason
for this and explain why this effect is observed with a t-butyl compound.

Solution. The normal mechanism for the hydrolysis of an alkyl halide is
S_N2 but with t-butyl chloride the reaction is S_N1, where the rate-determining
step is heterolysis of the carbon–chlorine bond, to give a carbonium ion.

$$Me_3C-Cl \xrightarrow{\text{Slow}} Me_3C^+ + Cl^-$$
$$Me_3C^+ + OH^- \xrightarrow{\text{Fast}} Me_3COH$$

As reaction with hydroxide occurs after the slow step, addition of potassium
hydroxide has no effect on the rate of reaction.

The t-butyl carbonium is more stable than similar ions formed from
secondary or primary alkyl halides and this is why the effect is observed

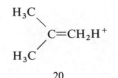

20

only with a *t*-butyl compound. Stabilization is probably due to hyper-conjugation. E. D. Hughes, *J. Chem. Soc.*, **1935**, 255.

22. The reaction between acetic anhydride and β-naphthol in acetic acid is catalysed by hydrogen chloride.

$$(CH_3CO)_2O + \text{[β-naphthol, OH]} \xrightarrow{HCl} \text{[naphthyl-OCOCH}_3\text{]} + CH_3CO_2H$$

A kinetic study showed the reaction to be first order in anhydride, naphthol, and hydrogen chloride. Addition of acetic anhydride containing ^{14}C resulted in rapid dispersion of the radioactive isotope throughout the solvent. Use these results to show that the acylating agent is acetyl chloride.

Solution. Acetyl chloride must be formed by reaction of acetic anhydride and hydrogen chloride.

$$(CH_3CO)_2O + HCl \underset{}{\overset{K}{\rightleftharpoons}} CH_3COCl + CH_3CO_2H$$

$$CH_3COCl + \text{Naphthol} \xrightarrow{k} \text{Products}$$

If the second step is slow the kinetic equation is as follows.

$$\text{Rate} = k[CH_3COCl][\text{Naphthol}]$$

$$= kK[(CH_3CO)_2O][HCl][\text{Naphthol}]$$

Therefore, the reaction is first order in each of the three reactants. The term $[CH_3CO_2H]$ does not appear as it is present in such large excess that its concentration remains effectively constant during the course of a kinetic run. Dispersion of the ^{14}C occurs owing to the rapid equilibrium step leading to formation of acetic acid. D. P. N. Satchell, *J. Chem. Soc.*, **1960**, 1752.

23. In the acid-catalysed chlorination of acetone the reaction is zero order in chlorine at high initial concentrations of chlorine but first order when the initial concentration is low. Explain this observation.

Solution. The slow step in the chlorination of acetone is acid-catalysed enolization and the reaction between enol and chlorine is fast, so the reaction is zero order in chlorine. However, at very low chlorine concentration, reaction between enol and chlorine becomes the slow step and

$$CH_3\overset{O}{\overset{\|}{C}}OCH_3 \xrightarrow{H^+} CH_2=\overset{OH}{\overset{|}{C}}-CH_3$$

$$CH_2=\overset{OH}{\overset{|}{C}}-CH_3 + Cl_2 \rightarrow CH_2Cl\overset{O}{\overset{\|}{C}}-CH_3 + HCl$$

the reaction is first order in chlorine. A. Lapworth, *J. Chem. Soc.*, **1904**, 30. R. P. Bell and K. Yates, *J. Chem. Soc.*, **1962**, 1931. (This historic paper by Lapworth provided the first great stimulus to the study of reaction mechanisms.)

24. A number of reactions were found to result in the production of an identical adduct with furan and another with cyclohexadiene. The relative rate of formation of the two adducts (k_{rel}) in the presence of the same mixture of furan and cyclohexadiene was measured, with the following results.

Reaction	k_{rel}

(a) Decomposition of 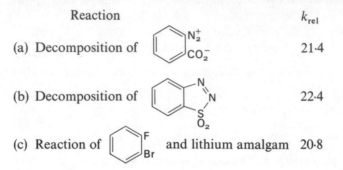 21·4

(b) Decomposition of 22·4

(c) Reaction of and lithium amalgam 20·8

What do these figures suggest?

Solution. The constancy of the value of k_{rel} for such diverse reactions suggests formation of a common intermediate, which then reacts competitively with furan and cyclohexadiene. The most likely species is

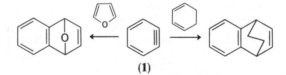

(1)

benzyne (**1**) which adds to furan and cyclohexadiene in a Diels–Alder reaction. R. Huisgen and R. Knorr, *Tetrahedron Letters*, **1963**, 1017.

25. Keto acids are fairly readily iodinated by molecular iodine and the mechanism appears to be the same as that for acetone.

$$CH_3COCH_2(CH_2)_nCO_2H + I_2 \rightarrow CH_3COCHI(CH_2)_nCO_2H + HI$$

The rate of reaction in the absence of a catalyst has been studied as a function of n, with the following results.

(a) Iodination of the anion:

n	1	2	3	4	10
$10^8 k \ \text{sec}^{-1}$	29·8	179	72	3·4	3·2

(b) Iodination of the ethyl ester:

n	1	2
$10^8 k \sec^{-1}$	0·20	0·32

What do these results indicate?

Solution. In the base-catalysed iodination of acetone the rate-determining step is proton removal to give a carbanion. The rate maximum with $n = 2$ suggests that the ionized carboxylate group may assist in the removal of a proton. This results in a six-membered cyclic transition state. There is then rapid attack of iodine on the resulting carbanion. With $n = 3$ or more a more strained transition state results. When there is no ionizable

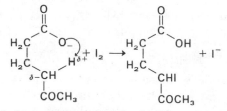

group (i.e. the ethyl ester) the compound with $n = 2$ does not show the same rate enhancement. R. P. Bell and M. A. D. Fleundy, *Trans. Faraday Soc.*, **59**, 1623 (1963). R. P. Bell and P. de Maria, *Trans. Faraday Soc.*, **66**, 930 (1970).

26. The product of the reaction of 7,8-diphenylbenzocyclobutane (**1**) and tetracyanoethylene (a good dienophile) is the adduct **2**.

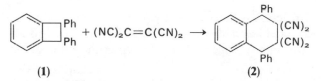

The rate of reaction is independent of the concentration of tetracyanoethylene and depends only on that of the 7,9-diphenylbenzocyclobutane. Suggest a possible intermediate in this reaction and indicate the rate-determining step.

Solution. The fact that tetracyanoethylene is a good dienophile suggests the formation of a conjugated diene from 7,8-diphenylbenzocyclobutane as an intermediate. Also, its formation must be slow, and reaction with tetracyanoethylene occurs after the rate-determining step. If this were not

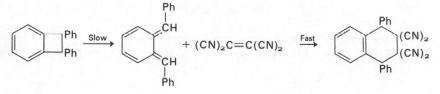

the case the concentration of tetracyanoethylene would affect the rate of reaction. The above seems the most likely scheme. R. Huisgen and H. Seidl, *Tetrahedron Letters*, **1964**, 3381.

27. Salt effects on the rate of hydrolysis of 4,4′-dimethylbenzhydryl chloride (1) in 85 % aqueous acetone have been studied. Explain the observation that, although bromide and azide ion have the same effect on the rate, the former does not affect the products but with the latter 64 % 4,4′-dimethylbenzhydryl azide is formed.

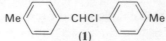

$$Me\text{—}\langle\rangle\text{—}CHCl\text{—}\langle\rangle\text{—}Me$$
(1)

Solution. Hydrolysis of 4,4′-dimethylbenzhydryl chloride is an S_N1 reaction, the rate-determining step being fission of the C—Cl bond.

$$(MeC_6H_4)_2CHCl \rightarrow (MeC_6H_4)_2CH^+ + Cl^-$$

Bromide and azide as salts affect the rate of ionization in the same way but the subsequent fate of the carbonium ion depends on the nucleophiles present. Bromide is a weak nucleophile and the main reaction is with water, but azide ion is a strong nucleophile and consequently reacts preferentially with the carbonium ion to give the azide. L. Bateman, E. D. Hughes, and C. K. Ingold, *J. Chem. Soc.*, **1940**, 974.

28. Hydrolysis of dimethylene chlorohydrin is a simple S_N2 reaction.

$$ClCH_2CH_2OH + H_2O \rightarrow HOCH_2CH_2OH + HCl$$

The rate of reaction is determined by following the appearance of chloride ion. A series of chlorohydrins $[Cl(CH_2)_nOH]$ were studied and the rate of reaction was found to depend markedly upon the value of n.

n	2	3	4	5
$10^5 k \text{ min}^{-1}$	1·82	7·79	1710	70

With $n = 4$ and 5 tetrahydrofuran and tetrahydropyran were detected as the products of reaction. Explain these observations.

Solution. With $n = 4$ and 5 there is neighbouring-group participation by the hydroxyl group which facilitates loss of chloride ion. The cyclic

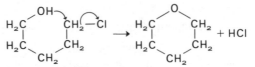

transition state in these cases is a five- or six-membered ring. H. W. Heine, A. D. Miller, W. H. Barton, and R. W. Greiner, *J. Amer. Chem. Soc.*, **75**, 4778 (1953).

Activation Parameters

Transition-state theory leads to the definition of a number of thermodynamic quantities relative to formation of the transition state (e.g. enthalpy of activation). Many research papers report values for these quantities, obtained from an Arrhenius plot, but they have proved of surprisingly little value in the diagnosis of reaction mechanism. Indeed, Professor Dewar has described measurements of the effect of temperature on reaction rates as a 'fetish' (*Molecular Orbital Theory of Organic Chemistry*, McGraw-Hill, New York, 1969, p. 283). This is, perhaps, overstating the case and a knowledge of particularly the entropy of activation ($\Delta S^{\ddagger}$) can be of value. The definition and use of these quantities is discussed in most texts. There are full accounts in Alder, Baker, and Brown, Gould, Frost, and Pearson, and Leffler and Grunwald. The values of $\Delta S^{\ddagger}$ in different types of acid-catalysed reactions are discussed by L. L. Schaleger and F. A. Long [*Advances in Physical Organic Chemistry* (Ed. V. Gold), Vol. 1, Academic Press, New York, 1963, p. 1]. The effect of pressure on reactions in solution has been reviewed by E. Whalley [*Advances in Physical Organic Chemistry* (Ed. V. Gold), Vol. 2, 1964, p. 93]. Several problems in Part 2 include the interpretation of activation parameters.

29. The acid-catalysed hydrolysis of 4-methoxybut-3-en-2-one (**1**) is associated with an entropy of activation of -26 e.u.

$$\text{MeOCH=CH}-\overset{\overset{\displaystyle O}{\|}}{\text{C}}\text{Me} + \text{H}_2\text{O} \xrightarrow{\text{H}^+} \underset{\text{H}}{\overset{\displaystyle O}{\diagdown}}\overset{\displaystyle}{\diagup}\text{C}-\text{CH=}\overset{\overset{\displaystyle OH}{|}}{\text{C}}\text{Me} + \text{MeOH}$$

(1)

Suggest a mechanism of reaction, indicating the rate-determining step.

Solution. If water is involved in the rate-determining step then it will suffer loss of translational and rotational freedom and lead to a more negative entropy of activation than in an A-1 reaction (i.e. monomolecular decomposition of the protonated substrate). A value of -26 e.u. is typical of a

$$\text{MeOCH=CH}-\overset{\overset{\displaystyle O}{\|}}{\text{C}}\text{Me} + \text{H}^+ \rightleftharpoons \text{MeOCH=CH}-\overset{\overset{\displaystyle{}^+\!OH}{\|}}{\text{C}}\text{Me} \rightleftharpoons \text{MeO}\overset{+}{\text{C}}\text{H}-\text{CH=}\overset{\overset{\displaystyle OH}{|}}{\text{C}}\text{Me}$$

$$\xleftarrow[\text{Slow}]{\text{H}_2\text{O}}$$

$$\text{MeOH} + \underset{\text{H}}{\overset{\displaystyle O}{\diagdown}}\overset{}{\diagup}\text{C}-\text{CH=}\overset{\overset{\displaystyle OH}{|}}{\text{C}}\text{Me} \xleftarrow{\text{Fast}} \underset{\text{HO}}{\overset{\displaystyle MeO}{\diagdown}}\overset{}{\diagup}\text{CH}-\text{CH=}\overset{\overset{\displaystyle OH}{|}}{\text{C}}\text{Me} + \text{H}^+$$

25

reaction involving water in the rate-determining step. L. R. Fedor and
J. McLaughlin, *J. Amer. Chem. Soc.*, **91**, 3594 (1969).

30. Comment on the observation that $\Delta S^{\ddagger}$ for the hydrolysis of *t*-butyl
trifluoroacetate is $+14 \cdot 8$ e.u. and that for methyl trifluoroacetate is $-32 \cdot 3$ e.u.

Solution. The large change in $\Delta S^{\ddagger}$ in going from *t*-butyl to methyl indicates
a change in mechanism. The large negative entropy of activation suggests
that a water molecule is involved in the rate-determining step (see previous
solution) and the mechanism for the methyl ester must be S_N2. The only
alternative for the *t*-butyl compound is an S_N1 mechanism but it is difficult
to give an interpretation to the positive entropy of activation. J. G. Martin
and J. M. W. Scott, *Chem. Ind. (London)*, **1967**, 665.

31. The hydrolysis of *p*-nitrophenyl-(*N,N*-dimethylamino)butyrate (**1**) is
associated with a small entropy of activation ($6 \cdot 4$ e.u.).

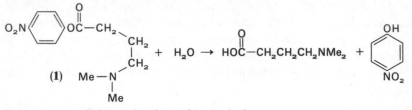

Suggest a possible mechanism of hydrolysis.

Solution. A small entropy of activation is often associated with a cyclic
transition state formed in an intramolecular reaction, as fewer degrees of
freedom are lost than in a bimolecular reaction. The dimethylamino
group in **1** is correctly situated to displace the *p*-nitrophenolate ion in an

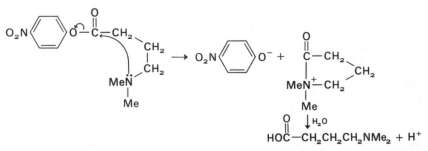

intramolecular process. T. C. Bruice and S. J. Benkovic, *J. Amer. Chem.
Soc.*, **85**, 1 (1963).

(This is a very small part of an extensive and elegant study, in which
inter- and intramolecular processes are compared with respect to rate
and activation parameters. The reason for the small entropy of activation

in an intramolecular reaction is discussed. The results are of great relevance to an understanding of the catalytic action of enzymes, where the first step is complexing of the reactants, so that an intermolecular reaction becomes essentially intramolecular.)

32. There is a rapid hydrogen exchange when 3,5,8,10-tetramethylaceheptylene is dissolved in trifluoroacetic acid.

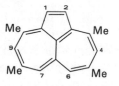

Exchange is fastest at the 1,2-positions, but the conjugate acid formed finally is that protonated at the 4,9- and/or 6,7-positions (it is not possible to distinguish them). Explain this result and draw reaction profiles for (a) hydrogen exchange and (b) formation of the conjugate acid.

Solution. Hydrogen exchange is kinetically controlled but the stability of the conjugate acid is thermodynamically controlled. The reaction profiles must have the form shown in Figure 2. Curve (a) is that for hydrogen exchange

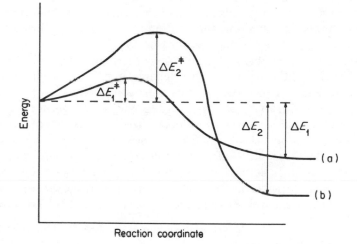

Figure 2. Reaction profiles for (a) hydrogen exchange and (b) formation of the conjugate acid.

at the 1,2-positions with a low activation energy ($\Delta E_1^{\ddagger}$), which makes the reaction fast, but not much energy (ΔE_1) is lost on formation of the conjugate acid. For hydrogen exchange at the 4,9- and 6,7-positions [curve (b)] there is a high activation energy $(\Delta E_2^{\ddagger})$, making the reaction slower, but the final product is more stable as its energy is much lower than that of the reactants (ΔE_2). The essential feature is that there is a cross-over of the two profiles. This is in violation of the 'chemical non-crossing rule' [R. D. Brown, *Quart. Rev. (London)*, **6**, 63 (1952)] but is consistent with HMO calculations. E. Haselbach, *Tetrahedron Letters*, **1970**, 1543.

33. Substitution by bulky groups at the *o*-position has a profound effect on the ionization of phenols, and not always in the same sense. The data given refer to the ionization values of a number of phenols in methanol. Rationalize the variation in the value of pK_a with substitution and show how this rationalization is consistent with changes in ΔH and $\Delta S°$.

	pK_a	ΔH kJ mol^{-1}	$-\Delta S°$ J deg^{-1} mol^{-1}
(a) phenol	14·46	35·7	157
(b) 4-*t*-butylphenol	14·65	36·7	157
(c) 2,6-di-*t*-butylphenol	17·30	35·2	213
(d) 4-nitrophenol	11·50	33·6	108
(e) 2,6-di-*t*-butyl-4-nitrophenol	10·99	35·2	92

Solution. The most likely explanation of the effect of bulky *o*-groups on ionization is hindered solvation and consequent destabilization of the anion. As the figures show, substitution at the 4-position has little effect on the pK_a but two *t*-butyl groups at the 2- and 6-positions reduce ionization considerably and there is less ordering of the solvent molecules by solvation of the anion. The large change in $\Delta S°$, although ΔH remains fairly constant, is consistent with this explanation, as an increase in entropy is associated with an increase in disorder. With 4-nitrophenol the negative charge of the anion is extensively delocalized and restriction of solvation at the oxygen atom is less significant. Substitution at the 2- and 6-positions has, therefore, very little effect. It is more difficult to understand why it should result in an actual decrease in the pK_a value. For a full discussion of the other possible factors, the original paper should be consulted. C. H. Rochester and B. Rossall, *Trans. Faraday Soc.*, **65**, 1004 (1969).

34. There are at least two possible mechanisms for the hydrolysis of the acetyl phosphate dianion.

$$CH_3CO{-}O{-}\overset{\overset{\textstyle O}{\|}}{\underset{\underset{\textstyle O^-}{}}{P}}{\overset{\textstyle O^-}{\diagup}} \quad + H_2O \rightarrow CH_3CO_2^- + H_2PO_4^-$$

(a) Attack of water directly on the P atom and displacement of acetate.

(b) Unimolecular decomposition to give metaphosphate ion followed by rapid attack of water.

$$CH_3CO_2PO_3^{2-} \xrightarrow{\text{Slow}} CH_3CO_2^- + PO_3^-$$
$$PO_3^- + H_2O \longrightarrow H_2PO_4^-$$

From a study of the effect of pressure on the rate of reaction, the volume of activation $(\Delta V^{\ddagger})$ was found to be $-1.0 \pm 1.0 \text{ cm}^3 \text{ mol}^{-1}$. By analogy with the effect of pressure on acid-catalysed reactions [E. Whalley, *Trans. Faraday Soc.*, **55**, 798 (1959)] with which mechanism is this value of $\Delta V^{\ddagger}$ consistent?

> *Solution.* The value of $\Delta V^{\ddagger}$ for a unimolecular A-1 mechanism is about zero, while that for an acid-catalysed reaction involving water in the rate-determining step (A-2) is negative by at least several $\text{cm}^3 \text{ mol}^{-1}$. Thus, the result obtained for this reaction is consistent with mechanism (b).
> G. Di Sabato, W. P. Jencks, and E. Whalley, *Can. J. Chem.*, **40**, 1220 (1962).

35. Photolysis of diethylhydroxylamine and di-*t*-butyl peroxide generates diethyl nitroxide radicals, which decay by self reaction.

$$2 \, Et_2NO^{\cdot} \rightarrow Et_2NOH + EtN(O) = CHCH_3$$

This process is readily followed by electron spin resonance. With dichloro-difluoromethane as solvent it is possible to study the reaction at very low temperatures and in the range -100 to $-145°$ the nitroxide radicals can be shown to be in equilibrium with a diamagnetic dimer but it is not known if this dimer is an intermediate in the above reaction. The radicals could decay according to the following equation.

$$2 \, Et_2NO \overset{K_1}{\rightleftharpoons} (Et_2NO)_2 \xrightarrow{k_2} EtN(O)=CHCH_3 + Et_2NOH$$

With isopentane as solvent the energy of activation was found to be *negative*. What does this suggest?

> *Solution.* A single-step process cannot possibly have a negative energy of activation but this is possible if there is a two-step mechanism, the first step of which is reversible, so the dimer may well be an intermediate. The variation of K_1 with temperature in isopentane is such that, on increasing the temperature, the equilibrium shifts to the left and this is not compensated for by a sufficiently large increase in k_2. Thus, the reaction becomes slower as the temperature is raised (i.e. a negative energy of activation).
> K. Adamic, D. F. Bowman, T. Gillan, and K. U. Ingold, *J. Amer. Chem. Soc.*, **93**, 902 (1971).

Salt and Solvent Effects

A comprehensive study of salt effects (e.g. the Debye–Hückel equation and the Brønsted salt effect equation) is more in the realm of physical than physical organic chemistry. However, salt effects can be used for the diagnosis of reaction mechanism but caution must be exercised as some ions have a very specific effect on a reaction. Ingold used salt effects extensively in his early work on reaction mechanisms and there is an account of this work in his text. They are discussed in some detail by Bell and by Hammett.

Although profoundly affecting both the rate and mechanism of many reactions, solvent changes are not greatly understood, particularly from a quantitative point of view. When it is considered that reactions involving bases go 10^{13} times faster in dimethyl sulphoxide than in methanol, the importance of the solvent becomes apparent. The matter is discussed in most texts but is particularly well covered by Kosower.

36. The rate of hydrolysis of 2,4,6-trimethylbenzoyl chloride in 95 % aqueous acetone is substantially increased by the addition of lithium perchlorate, while that of *p*-nitrobenzoyl chloride is reduced. Explain this observation.

Solution. The most likely explanation is that the mechanism of hydrolysis of 2,4,6-trimethylbenzoyl chloride is S_N1, while that of *p*-nitrobenzoyl

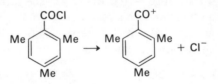

chloride is S_N2. In an S_N1 mechanism the rate-determining step is ionization and, as charge is created in the transition state, addition of a salt will increase the rate.

The S_N2 mechanism is attack of water on the carbonyl group and,

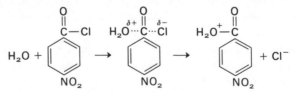

although charge is created in the transition state, the separation is much smaller than in an S_N1 reaction and the salt effect should be much less but still positive. In this example the rate is actually reduced by addition of lithium perchlorate. The lithium ion appears to have a specific effect and may lower the concentration of water by hydration, thus reducing the rate of reaction. This specific effect may not apply in more aqueous media. R. F. Hudson and G. Moss, *J. Chem. Soc.*, **1964**, 2982.

37. The rate of hydrolysis of benzoyl chloride is increased by different amounts on addition of equimolar quantities of potassium nitrate and lithium bromide. Suggest an explanation.

Solution. According to the Brønsted equation for salt effects, the size of the effect should depend only on the charge of the ions. As that does not apply in this case some other effect must occur. The effect of addition of nitrate is a simple salt effect but bromide reacts with the benzyl chloride to give benzoyl bromide and this hydrolyses more rapidly than the chloride. B. L. Archer, R. F. Hudson, and J. E. Wardill, *J. Chem. Soc.*, **1953**, 888.

38. Hydrolysis of substituted benzoic anhydrides is catalysed by strong acids and this catalysis is affected by addition of an inert salt. Allowing for a small spontaneous (i.e. uncatalysed) reaction, the rate equation in the presence of an excess of water is the following.

$$\text{Rate} = k[\text{HClO}_4][\text{Anhydride}]$$

The effect of adding LiClO_4 on the value of k at constant acid concentration ($[\text{HClO}_4] = 0.50 \text{ M}$) for a number of substituted benzoic anhydrides is given in the table.

$k \text{ l mol}^{-1} \text{ min}^{-1}$

$[\text{LiClO}_4]\text{M}$	p-MeO	p-Me	H	p-Cl
0	7.6	7.2	14.6	22.6
0.50	16.4	—	15.8	19.8
1.00	35	10.2	—	18.4
1.50	—	19.0	16.0	15.6
2.00	202	—	19.0	—
2.34	340	50	20.2	14.0

There are two possible mechanisms for acid-catalysed hydrolysis of these anhydrides (A-1 and A-2).

$$(\text{RCO})_2\text{O} + \text{H}^+ \rightleftharpoons (\text{RCO})_2\text{OH}^+$$

A-1 $\quad \left\{ \begin{array}{l} (\text{RCO})_2\text{OH}^+ \xrightarrow{\text{Slow}} \text{RCO}^+ + \text{RCO}_2\text{H} \\ \text{RCO}^+ + \text{H}_2\text{O} \xrightarrow{\text{Fast}} \text{RCO}_2\text{H} + \text{H}^+ \end{array} \right.$

A-2 $\quad (\text{RCO})_2\text{OH}^+ + \text{H}_2\text{O} \xrightarrow{\text{Slow}} 2\,\text{RCO}_2\text{H} + \text{H}^+$

Discuss the occurrence of these two mechanisms in the light of the observed salt effects.

Solution. The *A*-1 mechanism leads to a concentration of charge in the transition state and, therefore, will be subject to a large, positive salt effect. The figures indicate that the *p*-MeO compound must react by this mechanism. With the other anhydrides the salt effect is much less, until with the *p*-Cl compound addition of $LiClO_4$ actually leads to a decrease in rate. This suggests an *A*-2 mechanism [see C. A. Bunton, J. H. Crabtree, and L. Robinson, *J. Amer. Chem. Soc.*, **90**, 1258 (1968)] or, at least, one which is intermediate between *A*-1 and *A*-2. The electron-donating properties of the MeO group delocalize the positive charge on the carbonium ion and thus enhance the *A*-1 mechanism.

A feature emerging from the figures given is that, in the absence of added $LiClO_4$, the chloro compound reacts faster than the *p*-MeO, while in 2·34 M $LiClO_4$ the reverse is the case. Can you explain this effect? G. Calvaruso and F. P. Cavasino, *J. Chem. Soc.* (*B*), **1971**, 483.

39. Benzoylmethylenetriphenylphosphorane reacts with phenyl azide to give a 1-phenyl-1,2,3-triazole.

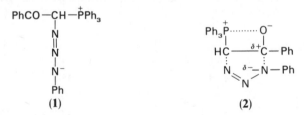

The mechanism of this reaction could be (a) a two-step process with **1** as an intermediate or (b) concerted cycloaddition via **2**.

The rate of reaction in three solvents of varying dielectric constant was measured with the following results.

Solvent	Dieletric constant	$k \, l \, mol^{-1} \, min^{-1}$
toluene	2·38	0·89
dimethylformamide	36·7	1·18
dimethylsulphoxide	48·9	1·65

With which mechanism are these results consistent?

Solution. Formation of **1** involves considerable charge separation and should be sensitive to the polarity of the medium: this is not reflected in the variation of k. There is much less charge separation in the formation of **2**, particularly as the ylid exists partly in its enolate form (**3**), and so the

$$\text{Ph}-\text{C}=\text{CH}-\overset{+}{\text{P}}\text{Ph}_3$$
$$| \\ \text{O}_-$$

(3)

small variation of k is consistent with mechanism (b). P. Ykman, G. L'Abbe, and G. Smets, *Tetrahedron*, **27**, 845 (1971).

40. Several attempts have been made to put solvent effects on reaction rates on a quantitative basis. Grunwald and Winstein used the hydrolysis of t-butyl chloride in 80% aqueous ethanol as a standard reaction because it was believed to be a limiting case of an S_N1 reaction. They defined a parameter Y derived from the rates of reaction of t-butyl chloride in various solvents.

$$Y = \log k_{\text{solvent}}^{t\text{-BuCl}} - \log k_{80\%\text{EtOH}}^{t\text{-BuCl}}$$

The slope of a plot of $\log k_{\text{obs}}$ against Y is m. 2-Benzamidoethyl bromide (**1**) undergoes a thermal cyclization reaction to give the compound **2**.

$$\text{PhCONHCH}_2\text{CH}_2\text{Br} \longrightarrow \text{PhC}\underset{\underset{\text{H}}{\text{N}-\text{CH}_2}}{\overset{\text{O}-\text{CH}_2}{\overset{+}{\diagup}}} \quad \text{Br}^-$$

(**1**)   (**2**)

The rate of this reaction in aqueous ethanol has been studied as a function of solvent composition at 25° with the following results.

% ethanol	100	90	80	70	60	50	40	30
$10^5 k_{\text{obs}}$ sec^{-1}	3·15	5·19	6·95	7·86	8·90	10·20	10·42	11·01

Plot $\log k_{\text{obs}}$ against the Winstein–Grunwald parameter Y for aqueous ethanol (see A. H. Fainberg and S. Winstein, *J. Amer. Chem. Soc.*, **78**, 2770 (1956)) and obtain the value of m for this reaction. By comparing this value with that for the ionization of t-butyl bromide ($m = 0·941$) and the solvolysis of ethyl bromide ($m = 0·343$), both in aqueous ethanol, suggest a mechanism for the reaction.

Solution. The plot of $\log k_{\text{obs}}$ against Y is rectilinear with $m = 0·13$, which is much smaller than that for the S_N1 reactions quoted above and less even than that for an externally induced S_N2 reaction. The cyclization reaction is therefore particularly insensitive to changes in solvent and this

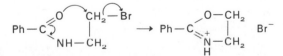

suggests an internal S_N2 reaction. F. L. Scott, E. J. Flynn, and D. F. Fenton, *J. Chem. Soc.* (*B*), **1971**, 277.

Isotopes

Isotopes may be used in two ways in mechanistic investigations: as tracers or for measuring the change in rate on isotopic substitution.

The principle behind tracer studies is very simple, although sometimes the experiments are difficult to perform because of the complicated degradative procedures necessary to locate the tracer atom. This is particularly true of biosynthetic studies, but, fortunately, these do not come within the scope of physical organic chemistry. The ready availability of a radioactive isotope of carbon (^{14}C) and the development of liquid scintillation counting techniques have been a great asset in mechanistic studies. All texts on reaction mechanisms give examples of the use of isotopic tracers and the subject has been reviewed by C. J. Collins [*Advances in Physical Organic Chemistry* (Ed. V. Gold), Vol. 2, Academic Press, New York, 1964, p. 1].

Kinetic isotope effects are of equal value as mechanistic probes but their interpretation is more difficult. There is an excellent account of the underlying quantum chemistry in Wiberg and the matter is also discussed by Bell. The most complete treatment is that of L. Melander (*Isotope Effects on Reaction Rates*, The Ronald Press, New York, 1960). In general, the effect of isotopic substitution on reaction rates is fairly obvious, the heavier isotope forming the stronger bond. The most complicated case is that of acid-catalysis where a change from H_2O to D_2O has been used to distinguish between general and specific acid-catalysis. This matter is discussed by Wiberg under the Brønsted catalysis law, in a review by the same author [*Chem. Rev.*, **55**, 713 (1955)], and by Bell. Problems on this topic can be found in the section on acid–base catalysis.

41. Rearrangement of phenylsulphamic acid to sulphanilic acid occurs in the presence of sulphuric acid.

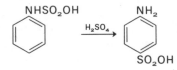

An *equimolar* mixture of phenylsulphamic acid and [^{35}S]H_2SO_4 showed 50% incorporation of ^{35}S in the resulting sulphanilic acid. Suggest a mechanism for this reaction.

Solution. Incorporation of ^{35}S into the product indicates that the reaction is *inter*molecular. A possible mechanism is initial protonation of the nitrogen followed by loss of SO_2OH^+, which then sulphonates the ring at the *p*-position.

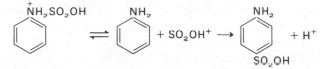

The absence of attack at the *o*-position may be due to steric factors. W. Spillane and F. L. Scott, *Tetrahedron Letters*, **24**, **1967**, 1251. (For an alternative mechanism see Z. Vrba and Z. J. Allan, *Tetrahedron Letters*, **1968**, 4507.)

42. Hydrolysis of phthalamic acid (**1**) to phthalic acid (**2**) was thought to involve elimination of ammonia and intermediate formation of phthalic anhydride.

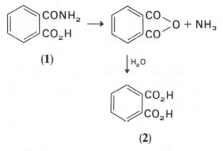

This possibility was investigated by an analysis of the products of reaction between phthalamic acid labelled with ^{13}C in the amide group and water enriched with ^{18}O. Show how this could demonstrate the intermediacy of phthalic anhydride and suggest how the products might be analysed.

Solution. The alternative to formation of phthalic anhydride is direct attack of water on the amide group [path (a)]. This would result in all the

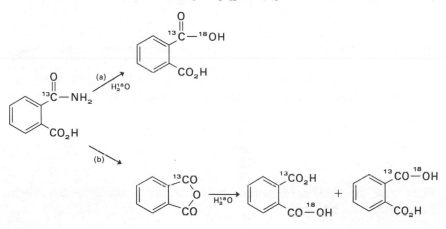

^{18}O occupying the carboxylic group labelled with ^{13}C. However, formation of the symmetrical anhydride leads to equal distribution of ^{18}O between the two carboxylic groups.

The product of reaction was analysed by mass spectroscopy. The phthalic acid was decarboxylated and the amount of CO_2 of mass 47 determined. Pathway (b) should produce half the amount of (a), and, by knowing the isotopic composition of the reactants, the pathway (b) was shown to be the correct one. M. L. Bender, Y.-L. Chow, and F. Chloupek, *J. Amer. Chem. Soc.*, **80**, 5380 (1958).

43. Irradiation of 2-phenylthiophen converts it into the 3-isomer. If the 2-carbon atom is labelled by ^{14}C, radioactivity is found at the 3-position after irradiation. Comment on this observation.

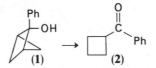

Solution. The most obvious mechanism for this reaction is dissociation to give phenyl radicals which then substitute at the 3-position. However, this cannot be correct as this would leave the radioactive carbon at the 2-position. Instead there must be complete reorganization of the thiophen molecule and a number of intermediates are possible. H. Wynberg, R. M. Kellogg, H. van Driel, and G. E. Beekhius, *J. Amer. Chem. Soc.*, **89**, 3501 (1967). H. Wynberg and H. van Driel, *Chem. Commun.*, **1966**, 203.

44*. One of the products resulting from the thermal rearrangement of 2-phenylbicyclo[1.1.1.]penta-2-ol (**1**) is cyclobutylphenyl ketone (**2**).

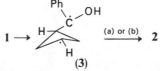

By analogy with other reactions, the mechanism is thought to be cleavage of the C—C bridgehead bond to give a diradical (**3**) [cf. S. W. Benson, *J. Chem. Phys.*, **34**, 521 (1961)] followed by either (a) a 1,3-H shift across the ring and rearrangement of the resulting vinyl alcohol or (b) a 1,5-H shift from the OH group.

Show how substitution of protium by deuterium at the 2-position might distinguish these possibilities.

Solution. Isotopic labelling would lead to two possible diradicals, **4** and **5**.

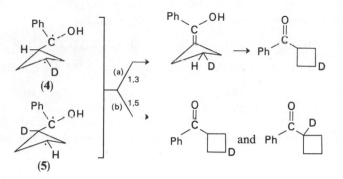

By route (a) there is only one possible product, but by route (b) the deuterium may end up on the carbon adjacent to the carbonyl group or on the opposite side of the ring. The latter was found to be the case, indicating a 1,5-H shift. A. Padwa and E. Alexander, *J. Amer. Chem. Soc.,* **92**, 5674 (1970).

45. In the presence of acetate ion, nitromethane reacts readily with bromine to give, initially, monobromonitromethane.

$$CH_3NO_2 + Br_2 \rightarrow CH_2BrNO_2 + HBr$$

The fully deuteriated compound (CD_3NO_2) reacts 6·6 times more slowly than the isotopically normal compound.

What is the rate-determining step in this reaction?

Solution. Clearly the C—H or C—D bond is broken in the rate-determining step and, as the C—D bond is stronger, the deuteriated compound reacts more slowly. The slow step is ionization of the nitromethane, catalysed by

$$O_2NCH_3 + CH_3CO_2^- \xrightarrow{Slow} O_2NCH_2^- + CH_3CO_2H$$

$$O_2NCH_2^- + Br_2 \xrightarrow{Fast} O_2NCH_2Br + Br^-$$

the acetate ion acting as a base, and the anion of nitromethane reacts rapidly with bromine. O. Reitz, *Z. Physik. Chem. Frankfurt,* **176**, 363 (1936).

46. Oxidation of isopropyl alcohol to acetone by acidified dichromate occurs via formation of a chromate ester. The rate of reaction was found to be first order in acid chromate ion ($HCrO_4^-$), alcohol, and hydrogen ion. The deuteriated compound ($Me_2CDOHCH_3$) was found to react more slowly than the isotopically normal compound. Suggest a mechanism for this reaction.

Solution. The rate-determining step must be removal of the secondary proton and this, together with formation of a chromate ester and catalysis by hydrogen ion, suggests the following mechanism.

$$HCrO_4^- + Me_2CHOH + H^+ \rightleftharpoons Me_2CHOCrO_3H + H_2O$$

$$H_2O + Me_2CHOCrO_3H \xrightarrow{\text{Slow}} Me_2C{=}O + H_3O^+ + HCrO_3^-$$

Oxidation of the alcohol results in reduction of the valency state of chromium. F. Holloway, M. Cohen, and F. H. Westheimer, *J. Amer. Chem. Soc.*, **73**, 65 (1951). [There has been a recent reinvestigation of this reaction but the nature of the rate-determining step has not been modified (K. B. Wiberg and S. K. Mukherjee, *J. Amer. Chem. Soc.*, **93**, 2543 (1971)).]

47. The enhanced rate of decomposition of peroxides in secondary alcohols is thought to be due to a chain reaction involving the peroxide and an α-hydroxyalkyl radical originating from the alcohol.

$$R_2'\dot{C}OH + ROOR \rightarrow R_2'CO + ROH + RO^{\cdot}$$

An attempt was made to determine the mechanism of this reaction by isotopic labelling. The decomposition of *t-butyl peroxide* in 2-butanol was found to be 1·63 times faster than in *O-d-2-butanol*, but for *acetyl peroxide* the rates are the same. What mechanisms are suggested by these observations?

Solution. A hydrogen isotope effect of 1·63 suggests that the slow step is a hydrogen transfer from the radical to the peroxide.

$$R_2'\dot{C}OH + Bu^tOOBu^t \xrightarrow{\text{Slow}} R_2'C{=}O + Bu^tOH + Bu^tO^{\cdot}$$

The absence of an isotope effect with acetyl peroxide means that this cannot be the rate-determining step: the reaction probably involves

$$R_2'\dot{C}OH + AcOOAc \xrightarrow{\text{Slow}} \underset{\underset{\displaystyle R_2'C{=}O + AcOH}{\big\downarrow \text{Fast}}}{\overset{\displaystyle |}{\underset{\displaystyle OAc}{R_2'COH}}} + AcO^{\cdot}$$

direct displacement of an acetyl radical by attack of the α-hydroxyalkyl radical on the peroxide. E. S. Huyser and A. A. Kahl, *J. Org. Chem.*, **35**, 3742 (1970).

48. Among possible mechanisms for the oxidation of ethanol by bromine are the following.

(a) $CH_3CH_2OH + Br_2 \xrightarrow{\text{Slow}} CH_3CH_2OBr + HBr$

$CH_3CH_2OBr \longrightarrow CH_3CHO + HBr$

(b) $CH_3CH_2OH + Br_2 \xrightarrow{\text{Slow}} CH_3\overset{+}{C}HOH + Br_2H^-$

$$CH_3\overset{+}{C}HOH \longrightarrow CH_3CHO + H^+$$

$$Br_2H^- \longrightarrow 2\,Br^- + H^+$$

A sample of partially tritiated ethanol (CH_3CHTOH) of activity $12\cdot3\mu$ Ci mmol^{-1} was incompletely oxidized by bromine leaving some ethanol unreacted. The activity of this was found to be $22\cdot0\ \mu$Ci mmol^{-1}.

With which mechanism is this observation consistent?

Solution. The increased activity of the unreacted ethanol indicates that the rate-determining step involves breaking of a $C-H$ bond. The $C-T$, being stronger, breaks less readily and so tritium is concentrated in unreacted material. Mechanism (b), but not (a), involves $C-H$ bond breaking in the slow step and so the observation is consistent with mechanism (b). L. Kaplan, *J. Amer. Chem. Soc.*, **76**, 4645 (1954).

49. The sulphonation of tritium-labelled bromobenzene is much slower than that of normal benzene, while nitration of nitrobenzene is unaffected by isotopic substitution on the aromatic ring. Explain these observations.

Solution. Electrophilic substitution is a two-step process and either k_1 or k_2 can be the slow, rate-determining step. If it is k_1 then there is no

hydrogen isotope effect (nitration) but if it is k_2 then isotopic substitution will produce a change in rate (sulphonation). L. Melander, *Acta Chem. Scand.*, **3**, 95 (1949). L. Melander, *Nature*, **163**, 599 (1949).

50. The reaction between styrene and tetracyanoethylene oxide results in 1,3-addition.

$$(1)$$

The rate of reaction is affected to a small extent by replacing the vinyl protons of styrene by deuterons and the numerical value of this secondary kinetic isotope effect is the same whichever of the three protons is replaced. Does this indicate a concerted or a two-step mechanism for 1,3-addition?

Solution. A possible two-step mechanism is the slow formation of the intermediate **2** (either as a dipolar species or a diradical, as shown), which then ring closes to give **1** as the second step. However, this would not result in an isotope effect for the α-hydrogen. The constant value of the isotope effect, independent of which proton is replaced, suggests a synchronous,

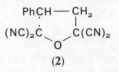

$$(2)$$

concerted mechanism where both the C—C bonds have formed to the same extent in the transition state. W. F. Bayne, *Tetrahedron Letters*, **1970**, 2263.

51. The hydrolysis of ethyl chloroformate is 1·9 times faster in H_2O than in D_2O. Suggest a mechanism based on this observation.

$$ClCO_2Et + H_2O \rightarrow EtOH + HCl + CO_2$$

Solution. The size of the kinetic isotope effect indicates that a C—H or a C—D bond is breaking in the transition state. This suggests two possible mechanisms.

(a) Addition–elimination

$$
\underset{\text{ClC—OEt}}{\overset{O}{\overset{\|}{}}} + H_2O \rightleftharpoons
\underset{\underset{\text{OH}}{|}}{\overset{\overset{\text{OH}}{|}}{\text{Cl—C—OEt}}}
\xrightarrow{\text{Slow}} HCl + EtOH + CO_2
$$

(b) Attack of water in an S_N2 reaction.

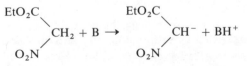

$$\rightarrow HCl + CO_2 + EtOH$$

(b) is really an extreme form of (a), where addition and elimination is occurring synchronously. The available data do not permit distinction between (a) and (b). A. Kivinen, *Suomen Kemistilehti*, **38B**, 205 (1965). [See also A. Queen, *Can. J. Chem.*, **45**, 1619 (1967).]

52*. It has been postulated that the kinetic hydrogen isotope effect (k_H/k_D) should be a maximum when the transition state is symmetrical [F. H. Westheimer, *Chem. Rev.*, **61**, 265 (1961)]. This has been tested by measuring the kinetic isotope effect for the base-catalysed ionization of ethyl nitroacetate with a variety of bases.

$$
\underset{O_2N}{\overset{EtO_2C}{>}}CH_2 + B \rightarrow
\underset{O_2N}{\overset{EtO_2C}{>}}CH^- + BH^+
$$

The following results were obtained for a number of bases (pK' = statistically corrected difference in pK_a between the substrate and base). Are the results consistent with the prediction?

Catalyst	$\Delta pK'$	k_H/k_D
(a) water	7·7	3·6
(b) 4-methylpyridine	0·1	9·1
(c) hydroxide	−10·0	4·6
(d) monochloroacetate	3·5	6·6
(e) phenoxide	−3·9	6·7
(f) acetate	3·5	7·7
(g) 2-chlorophenoxide	−2·3	8·1

Solution. The transition state will be symmetrical when the pK_a of the substrate equals that of the base removing the proton (i.e. when $\Delta pK'$ is zero).

As the graph indicates (Figure 3) the value of k_H/k_D does reach a maximum in the region of $\Delta pK' = 0$ and thus the results are consistent with the conclusion. D. J. Barnes and R. P. Bell, *Proc. Roy. Soc. A*, **318**, 421 (1970). [This interpretation of the size of the isotope effect has been challenged by F. G. Bordwell and W. J. Boyle (*J. Amer. Chem. Soc.*, **93**, 512 (1971)) but R. P. Bell and F. A. Long, and other workers, have found support for Westheimer's postulate.]

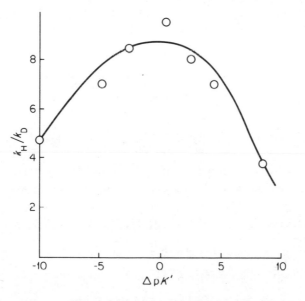

Figure 3. Plot of k_H/k_D versus $\Delta pK'$.

Acid–Base Catalysis

This topic has concerned physical organic chemists since the genesis of the subject in the 1930's. Interest remains unabated with the discovery of the relevance of this topic to enzymic catalysis. The classic work on the subject is that of Bell and there is a shorter discussion in Hine. There are two major works showing the importance of this topic in mechanistic biological chemistry: T. C. Bruice and S. J. Benkovic, *Bioorganic Mechanisms*, Benjamin, New York, 1966, and W. P. Jencks, *Catalysis in Chemistry and Enzymology*, McGraw-Hill, New York, 1969.

Before commencing the problems the student should have a clear understanding of the following terms: general and specific acid-catalysis, general and specific base-catalysis, and nucleophilic catalysis.

53. In aqueous solution acetaldehyde is slowly hydrated.

$$CH_3CHO + H_2O \rightarrow CH_3CH\begin{array}{c} OH \\ \diagup \\ \diagdown \\ OH \end{array}$$

In an acetate buffer the reaction is subject to acid- and base-catalysis. The first-order rate constants (k_{obs}), in two different acetate buffers, of known hydrogen ion concentration, were measured with the following results (r = buffer ratio $[CH_3CO_2H]/[CH_3CO_2^-]$).

(a) $[H^+] = 3.36 \times 10^{-6}\,M$ $\qquad\qquad\qquad r = 0.118$

$10^3[CH_3CO_2H]\,M$	2.7	4.9	6.9	9.0	10.9	
$10^2 k_{obs}\,min^{-1}$	6.6	8.7	9.9	11.6	12.7	

(b) $[H^+] = 8.78 \times 10^{-6}\,M$ $\qquad\qquad\qquad r = 0.308$

$10^3[CH_3CO_2H]\,M$	3.0	4.7	7.4	8.7	11.3	15.2
$10^2 k_{obs}\,min^{-1}$	8.2	9.3	10.2	10.6	12.3	13.4

Catalysis by hydroxide ion is known to be negligible but there is catalysis by hydrogen ions, acetic acid, and acetate ions, as well as a spontaneous reaction:

i.e. $k_{obs} = k_0 + k_1[H^+] + k_2[CH_3CO_2H] + k_3[CH_3CO_2^-]$

From the data given calculate the values of the rate constants.

Solution. Substituting for $[CH_3CO_2^-]$ in the equation gives

$$k_{obs} = k_0 + k_1[H^+] + [CH_3CO_2H](k_2 + k_3/r)$$

For each buffer $[H^+]$ is constant and a plot of k_{obs} versus $[CH_3CO_2H]$ gives a line of slope $(k_2 + k_3/r)$ and an intercept of $(k_0 + k_1[H^+])$. The two slopes are (a) 4·6 and (b) 7·5. By elimination of k_2, and substitution of the appropriate value of r, this gives $k_3 = 0·55 \, l \, mol^{-1} \, min^{-1}$ and then $k_2 = 2·8 \, l \, mol^{-1} \, min^{-1}$. The two intercepts are (a) 47 and (b) 69. Again by elimination of k_0 this gives $k_1 = 4 \times 10^3 \, l \, mol^{-1} \, min^{-1}$ and then $k_0 = 3 \times 10^{-2} \, min^{-1}$.

All the figures given are approximate as only a selection of the available data has been provided. In the original paper several other acetate buffers are used and this permits calculation of more accurate values. R. P. Bell and B. de B. Darwent, *Trans. Faraday Soc.*, **46**, 34 (1950).

54. The hydrolysis of *p*-nitrophenyl acetate is catalysed by acetate ion.

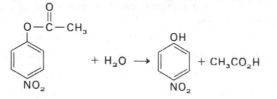

In the presence of aniline, there is spectroscopic evidence for the production of acetanilide. Does this indicate that the acetate ion acts by general base- or by nucleophilic catalysis?

Solution. General base-catalysis would have the following form:

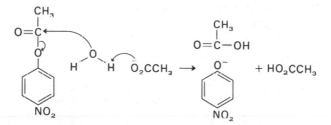

and there is no obvious reason for the formation of acetanilide.

Nucleophilic catalysis would result in the formation of acetic anhydride:

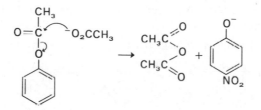

and this reacts preferentially with aniline (rather than water) to give acetanilide. Thus the evidence is in favour of nucleophilic catalysis. A. R. Butler and V. Gold, *J. Chem. Soc.*, **1962**, 1334.

55. Activated esters like ethyl difluoroacetate are very susceptible to hydrolysis. The following results were obtained for the rate of reaction in acetate buffers.

pH	[AcOH]M	[AcO⁻]M	k_{obs}min⁻¹
4·25	0·03	0·07	0·006
4·25	0·12	0·28	0·014
4·25	0·24	0·56	0·025
4·93	0·07	0·03	0·004
4·93	0·28	0·12	0·008
4·93	0·80	0·24	0·012

From these figures show that the reaction is not subject to specific or general acid-catalysis but there is a spontaneous (i.e. uncatalysed) reaction (k_0) and an acetate catalysed one (k_{OAc^-}).

Using D_2O as solvent $k_0 = 0.0016 \text{ min}^{-1}$ and $k_{OAc^-} = 0.0141 \text{ l mol}^{-1} \text{ min}^{-1}$. Do these results indicate nucleophilic or general base-catalysis?

Solution. The absence of specific or general acid-catalysis means there is no catalysis by hydrogen ions or undissociated acetic acid. Therefore, the rate of reaction should be directly proportional to the acetate ion concentration. A plot of k_{obs} versus [AcO⁻] is linear and independent of the pH. There is an intercept at [AcO⁻] = 0, indicating an uncatalysed reaction ($k_0 = 0.0034 \text{ min}^{-1}$). The slope of this line gives $k_{OAc^-} = 0.042 \text{ l mol}^{-1} \text{ min}^{-1}$.

The reduction in rate on changing to D_2O as solvent indicates that, in both the spontaneous and acetate-catalysed reaction, a O—H or O—D bond is being broken in the rate-determining step. This means general base-catalysis rather than nucleophilic.

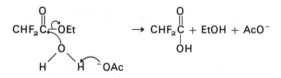

In the spontaneous reaction a second molecule of D_2O probably replaces acetate ion as the base. W. P. Jencks and J. Carriuolo, *J. Amer. Chem. Soc.*, **83**, 1743 (1961).

56. Hydrolysis of α-acetoxy-*p*-nitrostyrene is acid-catalysed.

In 6% sulphuric acid there is a kinetic isotope effect $k(H_2O)/k(D_2O)$ of 0·75 but in 69% sulphuric acid the size of this effect has changed to 3·25. What may be deduced about the mechanism of hydrolysis from this change?

Solution. The inversion of the kinetic isotope effect indicates a change of mechanism.

In dilute acid the mechanism is the same as that for normal ester hydrolysis, i.e. attack of water on the protonated form of the ester. D_3O^+ is a stronger acid than H_3O^+ and there will be a higher concentration of protonated ester in D_2O than H_2O, so the rate will be faster in the D_2O.

In more concentrated acid the rate is *slower* in D_2O than H_2O. This indicates that the rate-determining step is protonation of the ester to give a carbonium ion, followed by rapid attack of water.

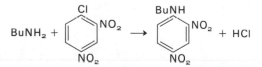

In this case the slow step involves fission of an O—H or O—D bond and, as the latter is stronger, the rate will be slower in D_2O. D. S. Noyce and R. M. Pollack, *J. Amer. Chem. Soc.*, **91**, 119 (1969).

57. There is reaction between n-butylamine and 2,4-dinitrochlorobenzene (DNCB) with replacement of chlorine.

BuNH$_2$ + (CI, NO$_2$, NO$_2$ on ring) → (BuNH, NO$_2$, NO$_2$ on ring) + HCl

The reaction was found to obey the following kinetic equation.

$$\text{Rate} = k_1[\text{BuNH}_2][\text{DNCB}] + k_2[\text{BuNH}_2]^2[\text{DNCB}]$$
$$+ k_3[\text{BuNH}_2][\text{DNCB}][\text{OH}^-]$$

What may be deduced from this? Suggest a possible mechanism.

Solution. The appearance of $[\text{BuNH}_2]^2$ in the second term and $[\text{OH}^-]$ in the third indicates base-catalysis where, in the second term, the base is a second molecule of butylamine. The important deduction is that there must be a two-step mechanism for a trimolecular collision is statistically impossible. The following mechanism is generally accepted.

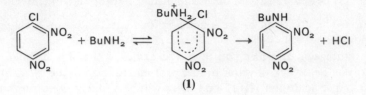

(1)

The breakdown of the intermediate **1** is spontaneous (k_1), catalysed by a second molecule of butylamine (k_2), or catalysed by OH^- (k_3). S. D. Ross, *J. Amer. Chem. Soc.*, **80**, 5319 (1958).

58. Acetone reacts with hydroxylamine to give an addition compound which then undergoes slow, acid-catalysed dehydration to form an oxime.

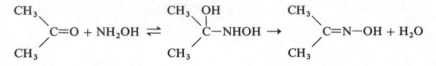

The variation of rate of reaction with pH is shown on the graph in Figure 4.

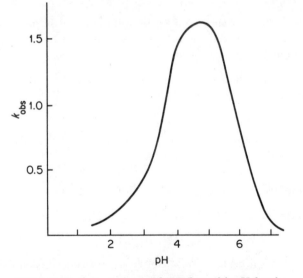

Figure 4. Variation of rate of reaction with pH for the reaction of acetone and hydroxylamine.

Explain the shape of this curve.

Solution. Above pH = 4·5 the slow step is dehydration which, as it is acid-catalysed, decreases with increasing pH. Below that pH, dehydration is so fast it is no longer rate-determining and the slow step is attack of free hydroxylamine on the carbonyl double bond. However, with increasing acidity more of the hydroxylamine becomes protonated and, therefore, unreactive and there is a consequent decrease in rate. W. P. Jencks, *J. Amer. Chem. Soc.*, **81**, 475 (1959).

59*. Hydrolysis of 2-amino-4,5-benzo-6-oxo-1,3-oxazine (**1**) gives *o*-ureido-benzoic acid.

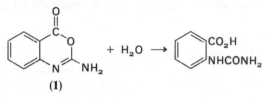

The pH rate profile for this reaction is as shown in Figure 5. Explain the shape of this curve.

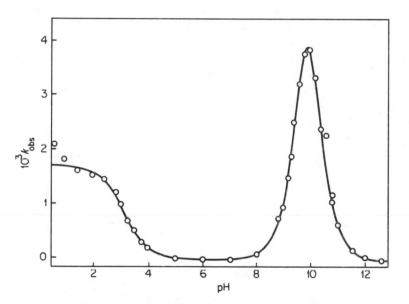

Figure 5. pH rate profile for the hydrolysis of 2-amino-4,5-benzo-6-oxo-1,3-oxazine.

Solution. The form of the pH rate profile may be explained by evoking four different forms of the substrate, related by differing degrees of proton loss.

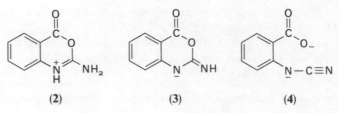

(2)   (3)   (4)

(a) At low pH the protonated form (2) is undergoing hydrolysis and its concentration decreases with increasing pH.

(b) In the plateau region (pH = 5 to 7) there is no protonation and the neutral form (1) is undergoing hydrolysis.

(c) From pH = 7 to 9·9 (the curve maximum) there is hydrolysis of 3, the concentration of which increases with increasing pH.

(d) The very rapid decrease above pH = 9·9 indicates formation of a species (4) which does not undergo hydrolysis.

The pH rate profile is analysed mathematically in the original paper and the analysis is consistent with the above qualitative description. However, it is possible to postulate other species which successfully explain the curve but the authors argue, from a variety of observations, that those shown above are chemically the most plausible. This reaction was studied as a possible model for acyl group transfer in the carbodiimide reaction and, possibly, CO_2 transfer in the biotincarboxylase reaction. A. F. Hegarty and T. C. Bruice, *J. Amer. Chem. Soc.*, **92**, 6561 (1970).

Acidity Functions

The molarity of a concentrated acid gives no measure of its ability to catalyse a reaction. This led Hammett in the 1930's to set up an acidity scale for concentrated acids based on indicator measurements, which measures not so much the concentration or activity of the hydrogen ion, but the ability of the solution to transfer a proton to a substrate which may then undergo reaction. There is an interesting historical note by Hammett [*J. Chem. Ed.*, **43**, 464 (1966)] and the subject is discussed in detail in his textbook. Most other books deal with the topic to some extent and there is an excellent monograph by C. H. Rochester (*Acidity Functions*, Academic Press, New York, 1970). There are two slightly dated, but otherwise excellent, reviews by M. Paul and F. A. Long [*Chem. Revs.*, **57**, 1, 935 (1957)] which describe not only the definition of the acidity scale but its use in determining reaction mechanisms.

The recent proliferation of acidity scales, using indicators other than the original primary amines, is discussed by Rochester and in a short review by C. J. O'Connor [*J. Chem. Ed.*, **46**, 686 (1969)]. For an account of Bunnett's *w* factor the original papers may be consulted [*J. Amer. Chem. Soc.*, **83**, 4968, 4973, 4978 (1961)].

The most doubtful part of the original work on acidity functions is the Hammett–Zucker hypothesis. It works in a few cases but is not generally applicable.

When a reaction displays a linear relationship between $\log k$ and $-H_0$ with a *slope of unity* then this is diagnostic and the reaction is A-1. An A-2 reaction *may* show a linear relationship between $\log k$ and $\log [H_3O^+]$, rather than $-H_0$, but this is not always the case.

60. Hydrolysis of β-propiolactone occurs in strong acid.

$$\begin{array}{l} CH_2-CH_2 \\ | \qquad\quad | \\ O\text{——}C=O \end{array} + H_2O \rightarrow \begin{array}{l} CH_2-CH_2-CO_2H \\ | \\ OH \end{array}$$

The variation of k_{obs} with $-H_0$ for the reaction in perchloric acid is given in the following table.

[HClO$_4$] M	1·83	2·60	2·75	3·26	3·93	4·53	5·36
$-H_0$	0·58	0·94	1·01	1·24	1·55	1·84	2·28
$10^3 k_{obs}$ min^{-1}	3·65	5·38	5·21	8·89	14·41	32·2	69·9

What is the mechanism of hydrolysis?

Solution. A plot of $\log k_{obs}$ versus $-H_0$ is linear with a slope of unity indicating an *A*-1 mechanism.

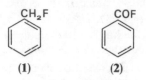

The slow step is cleavage of the C—O bond to form an acylium ion. F. A. Long and M. Purchase, *J. Amer. Chem. Soc.*, **72**, 3267 (1950).

61*. The hydrolyses of benzyl fluoride (**1**) and benzoyl fluoride (**2**) are both catalysed by perchloric acid. Variation of the rate of reaction with acid concentration is given in the following tables.

CH$_2$F   COF

(1)   (2)

(a) Benzyl fluoride in aqueous acetone at 50°.

[HClO$_4$] M	0·1	0·5	1·0	2·0	3·0	4·0	5·0
H_0	1·0	0·26	−0·12	−0·66	−1·13	−1·59	−2·06
$10^6 k_{obs}$ sec^{-1}	1·6	11·9	28·4	102	351	1160	4200

(b) Benzoyl fluoride in aqueous dioxan at 25°.

[HClO$_4$] M	0·24	0·46	0·86	1·38
H_0	1·90	1·48	0·90	0·34
$10^5 k_{obs}$ sec^{-1}	293	386	654	972

By correlation of rate constant with acidity of the medium, compare the mechanisms of these two reactions.

Solution. A comparison of these two reactions is one of the few examples of the successful application of the Hammett–Zucker hypothesis. For benzyl fluoride there is a linear relationship between $\log k_{obs}$ and $-H_0$ with a slope of unity, indicating an *A*-1 mechanism.

$$PhCH_2 + H^+ \rightleftharpoons PhCH_2FH^+$$
$$PhCH_2FH^+ \xrightarrow{\text{Slow}} PhCH_2^+ + HF$$
$$PhCH_2^+ + H_2O \longrightarrow PhCH_2OH + H^+$$

With benzoyl fluoride the relationship between $\log k_{obs}$ and H_0 is non-linear but there is a linear relationship between k_{obs} and the molarity of perchloric acid. This indicates an A-2 mechanism.

$$PhCOF + H^+ \rightleftharpoons PhCOFH^+$$

$$PhCOFH^+ + H_2O \xrightarrow{\text{Slow}} PhCO_2H_2^+ + HF$$

Can you suggest a reason for the change in mechanism? C. G. Swain and R. E. T. Spalding, *J. Amer. Chem. Soc.*, **82**, 6104 (1960). D. P. N. Satchell, *J. Chem. Soc.*, **1963**, 555.

62. Anilines are readily brominated by molecular bromine. In the presence of perchloric acid the kinetics of the reaction are complicated by protonation of the aniline so that it is present in two forms. However, bromination of 2,6-diethylaniline obeys the following simple kinetic expression.

$$\text{Rate} = k_2 [\text{An}]_{\text{st}} [\text{Br}_2]$$

$[\text{An}]_{\text{st}}$ is the stoicheiometric concentration of 2,6-diethylaniline. From the values of k_2 given in the table show that it is the free base and not the protonated aniline which is undergoing reaction.

$[\text{HClO}_4]$ M	4·70	5·56	6·71	7·49	8·15	8·46	8·60
$-H_0$	2·08	2·60	3·35	4·00	4·45	4·68	4·80
k_2 l mol^{-1} sec^{-1}	1165	440	70·6	16·1	4·80	2·30	1·76

2,6-Diethylaniline is so basic that the concentration of the protonated form $[\text{AnH}^+]$ can be put equal to $[\text{An}]_{\text{st}}$. However, this does not prevent the very small concentration of free base being kinetically important.

Solution. Consider protonation of the aniline and attack of bromine on the unprotonated residue.

$$\text{An} + \text{H}^+ \xrightarrow{K} \text{AnH}^+$$

$$\text{An} + \text{Br}_2 \xrightarrow{k} \text{Products}$$

$$\text{Rate} = k[\text{An}][\text{Br}_2]$$

$$= \frac{k[\text{AnH}^+][\text{Br}_2]}{K[\text{H}^+]}$$

Put $[\text{AnH}^+] = [\text{An}]_{\text{st}}$ and $[\text{H}^+] = h_0$.

$$\text{Rate} = \frac{k}{Kh_0}[\text{An}]_{\text{st}}[\text{Br}_2]$$

$$k_2 = k/Kh_0$$

$$\log k_2 = \log k/K - \log h_0$$

$$= \log k/K + H_0$$

These results for 2,6-diethylaniline are in agreement with this equation and a plot of $\log k_2$ against H_0 is linear with a slope of unity. R. P. Bell and P. De Maria, *J. Chem. Soc.* (*B*), **1969**, 1057.

63*. From a number of observations it was thought that the acid-catalysed hydrolyses of dioxolanes (**1**) and dioxolones (**2**) occur by different mechanisms.

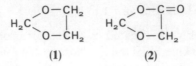

(**1**)   (**2**)

The following values for the Bunnett w factors were obtained.
(a) 4-Methyldioxolane $-2\cdot8$.
(b) 5-Methyldioxolone $+4\cdot8$.
By reference to the summary given by Bunnett [*J. Amer. Chem. Soc.*, **83**, 4968 (1961)] suggest mechanisms for these hydrolyses.

Solution. (a) A w factor of $-2\cdot8$ is normal for an *A*-1 reaction, in which water is not involved in the rate-determining step.

$$H_2C \overset{O-CH_2}{\underset{O-CHMe}{<\;|}} + H^+ \rightleftharpoons H_2C \overset{O-CH_2}{\underset{\overset{+}{O}-CHMe}{<\;|}} \xrightarrow{\text{Slow}} H_2\overset{+}{C}OCH_2CHMeOH$$

(b) A w factor of $+4\cdot8$ is characteristic of ester hydrolysis of the $A_{AC}2$ type, i.e. attack of water on the protonated substrate.

$$H_2C \overset{O-C=O}{\underset{O-CHMe}{<\;|}} + H^+ \rightleftharpoons H_2C \overset{O-C=O}{\underset{\overset{+}{O}-CHMe}{<\;|}} + H_2O \xrightarrow{\text{Slow}} \begin{matrix} HO-C=O \\ | \\ HO-CHMe \\ + HCHO + H^+ \end{matrix}$$

The exact position of protonation is not fixed. P. Salomaa, *Acta Chem. Scand.*, **20**, 1263 (1966). [In the original paper the hydrolysis of 2-substituted dioxolones is considered, with a w value of about $+1\cdot0$, but the interpretation of the mechanism on this criterion alone is difficult. The use of the Bunnett w factor is somewhat limited. It is very good for open-chain compounds of similar type but in its application to five- and six-membered rings many anomalies are encountered. (The author is grateful to Professor Salomaa for this comment.)]

Brønsted Catalysis Law

It is not surprising that the catalytic power of an acid or base is related to its pK_a and the Brønsted catalysis law is another example of a linear free energy relationship, of which the most well-known case is the Hammett $\rho\sigma$ equation. The topic is covered in detail by Hammett, by Bell, and by Alder, Baker, and Brown. The interpretation given to the size of the Brønsted coefficient α is discussed by the last of these authors and, in more detail, by V. Gold and D. C. A. Waterman (*J. Chem. Soc. (B)*, **1968**, 849).

64. The decomposition of nitramide is catalysed by bases.

$$H_2NNO_2 \xrightarrow{k} N_2O + H_2O$$

The following rates were obtained for a number of bases. Show that they obey the Brønsted catalysis law and determine the value of β for this reaction.

Base	pK_a	$k\,\mathrm{l\,mol^{-1}\,min^{-1}}$
(a) *p*-toluidine	5·12	1·16
(b) *m*-toluidine	4·69	0·64
(c) aniline	4·58	0·54
(d) *o*-toluidine	4·39	0·38
(e) *p*-chloroaniline	3·98	0·21
(f) *m*-chloroaniline	3·34	0·081
(g) *o*-chloroaniline	2·64	0·018

Solution. A graph of pK_a versus $\log k$ is linear (Figure 6).

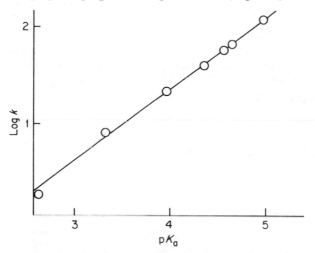

Figure 6. Graph of pK_a versus $\log k$ for the decomposition of nitramide.

The slope of this line ($= \beta$) is 0·73. J. N. Brønsted and K. J. Penderson, *Z. Physik. Chem.*, **1924**, 108, 185.

65. The rate-determining step in the base-catalysed iodination of a ketone is abstraction of a proton by the base (B) to give an anion.

$$CH_3COCH_3 + B \xrightarrow{\text{Slow}} CH_3COCH_2^- + BH^+$$

$$CH_3COCH_2^- + I_2 \xrightarrow{\text{Fast}} CH_3COCH_2I + I^-$$

Values of the second-order rate constants for this reaction for a number of bases were obtained using acetone (**1**) and isopropyl methyl ketone (**2**) as substrates. By using the Brønsted catalysis law show that this reaction may be subject to steric inhibition.

		$10^6 k \, l \, mol^{-1} \, sec^{-1}$	
Base	pK_b	**(1)**	**(2)**
pyridine	5·22	5·7	1·84
2-methylpyridine	5·96	15·2	4·2
3-methylpyridine	5·63	13·4	4·8
4-methylpyridine	5·98	20·4	7·1
2,6-dimethylpyridine	6·72	10·2	2·6
3,4-dimethylpyridine	6·46	38	16·3
3,5-dimethylpyridine	6·15	29	10·8
2,4,6-trimethylpyridine	7·59	18·5	5·4

Solution. For the structurally similar bases used the Brønsted catalysis law should apply. This is true for the reaction of both **1** and **2**, except that the points for 2,6-dimethylpyridine and 2,4,6-trimethylpyridine, and to a lesser extent 2-methylpyridine, fall well below the line. The only feature these bases have in common is a substituent next to the basic site and their decreased efficiency as base catalysts must be due to steric inhibition of proton transfer. The decreased efficiency is greater in the case of **2** than **1**, which is consistent with this explanation. J. A. Feather and V. Gold, *J. Chem. Soc.*, **1965**, 1752.

Complex Formation

The formation of complexes in organic chemistry is very common and their role in affecting reactivity is being increasingly understood. There is an excellent review on this subject by D. A. Banthorpe [*Chem. Rev.*, **70**, 295 (1970)]. Among textbooks on the subject two may be mentioned: R. Foster, *Organic Charge-Transfer Complexes*, Academic Press, New York, 1969 and L. J. Andrews and R. M. Keefer, *Molecular Complexes in Organic Chemistry*, Holden-Day, San Francisco, 1964.

66*. The hydrolysis of *N*-(indole-3-acryloyl)imidazole (**1**) in water is a *pseudo* first-order reaction (k_{obs}). Addition of 3,5-dinitrobenzoate ion (B)

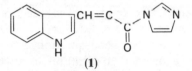

(1)

leads to formation of a charge-transfer complex (C) in an equilibrium process and the rate of hydrolysis is affected in the following manner.

[B] M	0.0120	0.0180	0.0300	0.0420	0.0601	0.0814	0.120
$10^3 k_{obs}$ s^{-1}	16.3	14.8	12.4	11.0	8.71	7.68	6.15

Show that the complex does not undergo hydrolysis and determine the association constant from the kinetic data. It is not possible to assume that the complex is present at very low concentration.

Solution. The charge-transfer complex is formed in an equilibrium process:

$$I + B \rightleftharpoons C$$

$$K = [C]/[I][B] \tag{1}$$

(I) is present in two forms, as free compound and as the complex.

$$[I]_{st} = [I] + [C] \tag{2}$$

where $[I]_{st}$ is the stoicheiometric concentration of (I). Substitution for $[C]$ from equation (1) gives the following expression.

$$[I]_{st} = [I](1 + K[B]) \tag{3}$$

If only the free form undergoes hydrolysis then the kinetic equation is as follows.

$$\text{Rate} = k[I] = \frac{k[I]_{st}}{(1 + K[B])} \tag{4}$$

The experimental rate expression is first order in $[I]_{st}$.

$$Rate = k_{obs}[I]_{st}$$

$$\therefore \quad k_{obs} = k/(1 + K[B]) \tag{5}$$

A plot of $1/k_{obs}$ against $[B]$ is linear with an intercept of 0.050×10^4 and a slope of 1.02×10^4. This gives $k = 20.0 \times 10^{-4}\,s^{-1}$ and $K = 20.2$ $l\,mol^{-1}$. F. M. Menger and M. L. Bender, *J. Amer. Chem. Soc.*, **88**, 131 (1966).

67. In most nitration reactions toluene reacts about thirty times faster than benzene. However, if the nitrating agent is nitronium tetrafluoroborate $(NO_2^+ BF_4^-)$ the reaction is extremely rapid and the relative reactivity is reduced to about two. This has been explained by assuming formation of a π complex, which then undergoes an internal reaction to give nitrobenzene and nitrotoluene [G. A. Olah and S. J. Kuhn, *J. Amer. Chem. Soc.*, **83**, 4564 (1961)] but this explanation has been questioned by several workers. In a recent paper it was reported that nitration of an excess of bibenzyl by nitronium tetrafluoroborate gave 50 to 70% dinitrobibenzyl and that the amount of the dinitrated product, compared to the mononitrated, depends on the rate of stirring as the reactants are mixed. Does this result support the intermediacy of a π complex? If not, what alternative does it suggest? With bibenzyl the separation of the benzene rings by two methylene groups means that nitration in one ring does not deactivate the other towards nitration.

Solution. The effect of stirring on the amount of dinitrobibenzyl formed suggests that π-complex formation does not explain the anomalous reactivities reported by Olah and his coworkers. The alternative explanation, entirely consistent with the above result, is that nitration by nitronium tetrafluoroborate is so fast that it is diffusion controlled and is faster than the mixing of the reactants. Although benzene is much less reactive than toluene it will be nitrated before more toluene is available by mixing. As an excess of bibenzyl was present, on statistical grounds, the mononitro compound should have predominated, but with poor mixing the second phenyl ring is attacked before more unsubstituted bibenzyl is available. P. F. Christy, J. H. Ridd, and N. D. Stears, *J. Chem. Soc.* (B), **1970**, 797. [The possibility that the stirring rate might affect the relative reactivities of aromatic compounds in nitration was first suggested by W. S. Tolgyesi, *Can. J. Chem.*, **43**, 343 (1965).]

Optical Activity

This property does not occupy in organic chemistry as important a place as it has in the past but it is not without value in the diagnosis of reaction mechanism. Its use is illustrated in the following examples.

68. Isotopic substitution of iodine in $(+)$-2-iodooctane by reaction with iodide ion causes racemization. Explain why racemization is complete when half the iodine has exchanged. Iodine exchange was followed by the use of a radioactive isotope.

Solution. Racemization occurs when an iodide ion attacks an iodooctane molecule and displaces the iodine already present with inversion of configuration (i.e. the Walden inversion). When half the iodooctane molecules have undergone this displacement reaction, racemization will be complete, and there will be a mixture of equal parts $(+)$-2-iodooctane and $(-)$-2-iodooctane. E. D. Hughes, F. Juliusburger, S. Masterman, B. Topley, and J. Weiss, *J. Chem. Soc.*, **1935**, 1525.

69. The reaction between water and β-butyrolactone is pH independent and must involve attack by an undissociated water molecule on the lactone. Hydrolysis by water containing ^{18}O results in an acid containing ^{18}O in the β-hydroxy group.

$$CH_3-CH-CH_2 + H_2^{18}O \rightarrow \overset{^{18}OH}{\underset{}{CH_3CH-CH_2CO_2H}}$$
$$\underset{O-C=O}{}$$

Also, $(+)$-butyrolactone hydrolyses to $(+)$-β-hydroxybutyric acid. Compare the configurations of the $(+)$-lactone and $(+)$-acid.

Solution. The appearance of ^{18}O in the hydroxy group indicates alkyl oxygen fission and inversion of configuration.

Therefore, $(+)$-butyrolactone and $(+)$-β-hydroxybutyric acid must have opposite configurations. A. R. Olson and R. J. Miller, *J. Amer. Chem. Soc.*, **60**, 2687 (1938). A. R. Olson and J. L. Hyde, *J. Amer. Chem. Soc.*, **53**, 2459 (1941).

70. One of the products of the thermal rearrangement of *trans*-1,2-divinyl-cyclobutane (**1**) is *cis,cis*-1,5-cyclooctadiene (**2**).

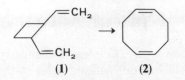

(1)   (2)

The most probable mechanism is formation of a diradical, followed by ring closure. An optically active sample of **1** was subjected to the usual reaction conditions and lost its optical activity at a rate just slightly faster than the rate of appearance of rearranged product and the recovered starting material was found to be partially racemized.

What may be deduced from this?

Solution. For ring closure to occur there must be rotation about the single bond and this will also racemize the material. From the similarity of the rates it is clear that the rate of ring closure in the intermediate is of the same order as rates of rotation about single bonds. G. S. Hammond and C. D. DeBoer, *J. Amer. Chem. Soc.*, **86**, 899 (1964).

Conservation of Orbital Symmetry

The Woodward–Hoffmann rules are one of the major advances in the understanding of reaction mechanisms of recent years. The original papers [R. B. Woodward and R. Hoffmann, *J. Amer. Chem. Soc.*, **87**, 395, 2046, 2511 (1965)] give a brief account but there is a fuller account, by the same authors, in *Angew. Chem. Intern. Ed. Engl.*, **8**, 781 (1969) and this has been published as a book (Academic Press, New York, 1970). The rules are too recent to be included in the standard texts, with the exception of Alder, Baker, and Brown, and Part III of Tedder, Nechvatal, Murray, and Carnduff, *Basic Organic Chemistry* (Wiley, London, 1970). There is a good introduction to the subject in a review by G. B. Gill [*Quart Rev.*, **22**, 338 (1968)] and it is treated more rigorously by Murrell, Kettle, and Tedder (*Valence Theory*, 2nd ed., Wiley, London, 1970).

71. Is the following reaction thermally or photochemically allowed?

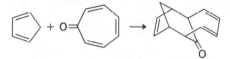

Solution. This is a $(\pi_s^6 + \pi_s^4)$ reaction and the number of π electrons involved (q) is ten. As $q/2$ is odd, the reaction is thermally allowed. Attempt to construct a correlation diagram for this reaction. R. C. Cookson, B. V. Drake, J. Hudec, and A. Morrison, *Chem. Commun.*, **1966**, 15.

72. Will the thermal and photochemical closures of a *cis,cis,cis,trans*-decatraene be conrotatory or disrotatory?

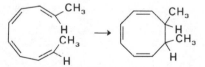

Solution. The general rule for an electrocyclic reaction of q π electrons in the ground state is that it will be disrotatory if $q/2$ is odd and conrotatory if $q/2$ is even. In this example $q = 8$, so the reaction is thermally conrotatory. In the first excited state the criteria are reversed and the reaction is photochemically disrotatory. R. Huisgen, A. Dahmen, and H. Huber, *J. Amer. Chem. Soc.*, **89**, 7130 (1967).

73. What product will result from the thermal isomerization of 7-methyl-1,3,5-cycloheptatriene?

Solution. The symmetry-allowed reaction is a [1,5] suprafacial shift and so the product of the reaction is 3-methyl-1,3,5-cycloheptatriene. K. W. Egger, *J. Amer. Chem. Soc.*, **89**, 3688 (1967).

74. The conservation of orbital symmetry suggests that [1,3] suprafacial shifts are symmetry forbidden while [1,5] shifts are allowed. Show how a consideration of the products of the thermal rearrangement of 7,8-dideuterio-cycloocta-1,3,5-triene might prove this prediction.

Solution. A series of reversible [1,3] sigmatropic shifts would result in distributing the deuterium statistically around the ring. However, a sequence of [1,5] shifts would place the deuterium in positions 3, 4, 7, and 8 only. The latter was found to be experimentally observed, thus confirming the prediction. W. R. Roth, *Ann.*, **671**, 25 (1964).

75. Why does the triene **1** not readily isomerize to toluene?

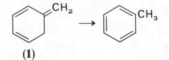

(1)

Solution. Such an isomerization involves a symmetry forbidden [1,3] shift. W. J. Bailey and R. A. Baylouny, *J. Org. Chem.*, **27**, 3476 (1962).

76. At 170° 1-mesityl-3-methylallene (**1**) isomerizes to a mixture of 2,5,7-trimethyl-1,2-dihydronaphthalene (**2**) and *cis*-1-mesitylbuta-1,3-diene (**3**) in a two-step process.

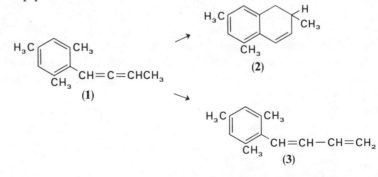

Suggest a mechanism for these reactions and describe the processes in terms of the conservation of orbital symmetry.

Solution. The first step is a [1,5 s]-sigmatropic shift to give **4**, the *trans* form of which exhibits a disrotatory ring closure to give **2** and the *cis*

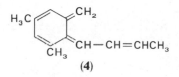

(4)

form undergoes a [1,7 a]-sigmatropic H-shift to give **3**. H. Heimgartner, J. Zsindely, H.-J. Hansen, and H. Schmid, *Helv. Chim. Acta,* **53**, 1212 (1970).

77. Predict the stereochemistry of the allyl cation obtained by the concerted ring opening and ionization of the three isomeric 2,3-dimethyl-1-cyclopropyl chlorides.

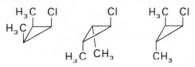

Solution. The opening of a cyclopropyl cation is a disrotatory process and which of the two disrotatory modes (i.e. the two substituent groups turning towards one another or away) depends upon the position of the leaving group (i.e. the chloride ion). Substituents on the same side of the three-membered ring as the leaving group rotate towards one another, whereas

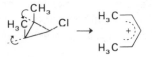

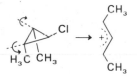

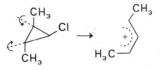

those on the other side rotate away. P. von R. Schleyer, T. M. Su, M. Saunders, and J. C. Rosenfeld, *J. Amer. Chem. Soc.,* **91**, 5174 (1969).

78. Explain the relative stability of 9,9'-dehydrodianthracene (**1**) which, it might be supposed, would rapidly isomerize to 9,9'-bianthryl (**2**).

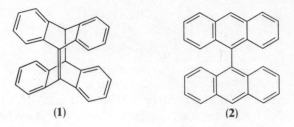

(1)   (2)

Solution. The symmetry allowed conrotatory transformation is opposed by a necessary twisting motion about the 9,9'-double bond, while the simpler disrotatory cleavage is symmetry forbidden. N. M. Weinshenker and F. D. Greene, *J. Amer. Chem. Soc.*, **90**, 506 (1968).

79. Comment on the observation that the thermal decomposition of *trans*-6,7-dimethylbicyclo[3,2,0]heptane gives mainly the *trans* form of but-2-ene

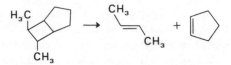

Solution. This product could result from a $(\sigma_s^2 + \sigma_a^2)$ concerted ring opening but such a reaction is symmetry forbidden. Therefore, the reaction cannot be concerted and a biradical intermediate has been suggested. A. T. Cooks, H. M. Frey, and I. D. R. Stevens, *Chem. Commun.*, **1969**, 458.

Part 2

Miscellaneous Problems

80. Hydrogen chloride is eliminated from DDT (1,1,1-trichloro-2,2-di-*p*-chlorophenylethane) by the action of ethoxide ion in alcoholic solution.

$$(ClC_6H_4)_2CH-CCl_3 \rightarrow (ClC_6H_4)_2C=CCl_2 + HCl$$

Do the following observations indicate an *E*1, *E*2, or *E*1*cB* mechanism?

(a) The rate of reaction is first order in both DDT and ethoxide ion.

(b) Introduction of deuterium at the 2-position reduces the rate by a factor of 3·8.

(c) Using tritiated ethanol (EtOT) as solvent does not introduce tritium into unreacted DDT.

Solution. The first-order dependence on ethoxide ion concentration shows the reaction cannot be *E*1. Reversible proton abstraction to form a carbanion ion (*E*1*cB* mechanism) should lead to incorporation of tritium

$$(ClC_6H_4)_2CH-CCl_3 \rightleftharpoons (ClC_6H_4)_2\bar{C}-CCl_3 + H^+$$

from the solvent into unreacted DDT but, as this does not occur, an *E*2 mechanism is indicated. An isotope effect of 3·8 is consistent with this as

$$(ClC_6H_4)_2 \underset{\substack{| \\ H \\ \curvearrowleft \\ {}^-OEt}}{C}\text{---}CCl_2\text{---}Cl \qquad (ClC_6H_4)_2\dot{C}=CCl_2 + Cl^-$$
$$\rightarrow \qquad\qquad +$$
$$\qquad\qquad\qquad EtOH$$

an *E*2 mechanism involves breaking a C—H or C—D bond in the rate-determining step and, as the latter is a stronger bond, the rate is consequently reduced. B. D. England and D. J. McLennan, *J. Chem. Soc. (B)*, **1966**, 696.

81. *N*-Nitroaniline in acid solution rearranges to *o*- and *p*-nitroaniline.

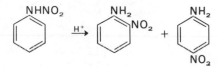

Suggest a mechanism for this rearrangement which is consistent with the following experimental observations.

(a) Radical scavengers do not affect the rate of reaction.

(b) In the presence of $H^{15}NO_2$ and $H^{15}NO_3$ no ^{15}N is found in the rearranged products.

(c) The kinetic expression for this reaction is

$$\text{Rate} = k[N\text{-Nitroaniline}]$$

(d) A study of the variation of k with acidity shows that $\log k$ is proportional to H_0.

(e) The rate of reaction in D_2O is 3·3 times that in H_2O.

(f) With N-nitroaniline deuteriated in the phenyl ring only the *ortho/para* ratio is changed and not the overall rate of reaction.

Solution. From (a) it is clear that free radicals are not involved in the rate-determining process. If the nitro group detached itself from the nitrogen and then attacked the ring, there should be equilibration with nitrous or nitric acid present. The absence of ^{15}N in the products indicates that this does not occur so the reaction must be *intra*molecular. The occurrence of acid-catalysis means that protonation of N-nitroaniline occurs and, as the reaction is faster in D_2O than H_2O, protonation must occur in a preequilibrium process. The slow step cannot be proton loss following attack of the migrating group on the phenyl ring as deuteriation does not affect the rate of reaction.

The exact mechanism of reaction is difficult to deduce but the above results indicate that it must consist of an intramolecular process involving protonated N-nitroaniline. The main difficulty is to explain how the

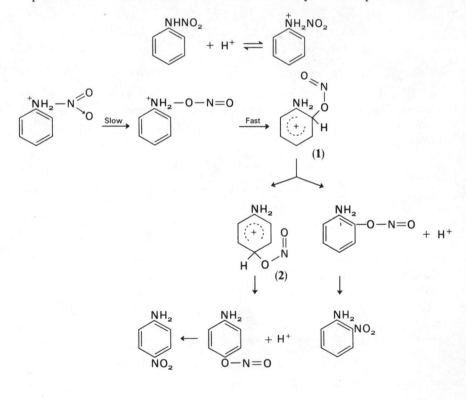

nitro group migrates to the *p*-position without becoming detached. The authors suggest a 'cartwheel' mechanism, shown on the previous page, in which the rate-determining step is isomerization of the nitro to nitrite. The nitrite group then attacks the *o*-position (1) and 'cartwheels' to the *p*-position (2). D. V. Banthorpe and J. A. Thomas, *J. Chem. Soc.*, **1965**, 7149.

82. Interpret the following observations on the hydrolysis of acetic anhydride in aqueous solution.

(a) The reaction is catalysed by acetate ion and this process is slower in D_2O than in H_2O.

(b) Spontaneous (i.e. uncatalysed) hydrolysis is also slower in D_2O than H_2O.

(c) Pyridine is an effective catalyst, but its effectiveness is reduced by the addition of acetate ion.

(d) Although a stronger base than pyridine, 2-methylpyridine is not a catalyst.

(e) Hydrolysis of trimethylacetic anhydride is not subject to catalysis by pyridine.

Solution. Acetate ion catalyses the reaction by assisting attack of water on the carbonyl group of the anhydride (i.e. general base-catalysis)

$$CH_3-\overset{O}{\underset{H-O}{\overset{\|}{C}}}-OCOCH_3 \rightarrow CH_3-\overset{O}{\overset{\|}{C}}-OH + {}^-OCOCH_3 + AcOH$$

For the spontaneous reaction a second molecule of water replaces the acetate ion, and in both cases an O—H or O—D bond is weakened in the transition state, giving rise to a kinetic isotope effect of greater than unity. Pyridine acts as a nucleophilic catalyst by reaction to give the acetyl-pyridinium ion (1) in an equilibrium step, which then reacts rapidly with water.

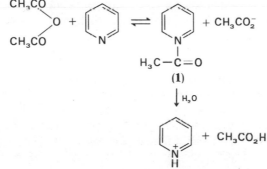

Addition of acetate ion reduces the effectiveness of pyridine by shifting the equilibrium to the left, and thus the concentration of the reactive intermediate (1) is reduced.

2-Methylpyridine cannot, for steric reasons, form an intermediate equivalent to 1 and is, therefore, not a catalyst. For similar steric reasons, trimethylacetic acid cannot form an equivalent intermediate with pyridine. A. R. Butler and V. Gold, *J. Chem. Soc.*, **1961**, 2305, 4362. [Recently the acetylpyridinium ion (1) has been observed directly by u.v. spectroscopy (A. R. Fersht and W. P. Jencks, *J. Amer. Chem. Soc.*, **92**, 5432 (1970)).]

83. Diazepines readily undergo electrophilic substitution and show many similarities with benzene compounds. With the latter compounds, exchange of an aromatic hydrogen is effected most readily by attack of a hydronium ion. However, with 2,3-dihydro-5,7-dimethyl-1,4-diazepinium perchlorate hydrogen exchange occurs, at the 6-position, in phosphate buffers of fairly high pH (i.e. low hydrogen ion concentration). The rate was found to be *independent* of the pH but did vary with the buffer concentration, as shown in the table.

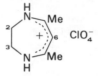

$[H_2PO_4^-]$M	$[HPO_4^{2-}]$M	$10^6 k_{obs} \, sec^{-1}$
0·349	0·351	214
0·462	0·092	279
0·426	0·043	262
0·070	0·352	47
0·034	0·343	23

What species in the buffer is responsible for hydrogen exchange? In the bromination of diazepines by molecular bromine in the presence of bromide ion, the tribromide ion (Br_3^-) appears to be an effective brominating agent, although it is generally ineffective with benzene compounds.

Rationalize these observations.

Solution. Inspection of the results indicates that the rate of hydrogen exchange is directly proportional to the concentration of $H_2PO_4^-$ and independent of the concentration of the hydrogen ion, which is the species generally responsible for hydrogen exchange in benzene compounds. So, for both hydrogen exchange and bromination the attacking species is negatively charged, whereas for benzene compounds it is positively charged (H_3O^+ and Br^+). This is due to the positive charge already present on the diazepinium ring making attack by another positive species electrostatically unfavourable. D. M. G. Lloyd and D. R. Marshall, *J. Chem. Soc.*, **1956**, 2597. R. P. Bell and D. R. Marshall, *J. Chem. Soc.*, **1964**, 2195. C. Barnett and J. Warkentin, *J. Chem. Soc. (B)*, **1968**, 1572.

84. The hydrolysis of [*N*-(3,5-dinitro-2-pyridyl)alanyl]glycine (**1**) is an acid-catalysed reaction.

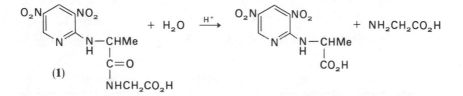

Discuss the mechanism of reaction in view of the following observations.

(a) There is a linear relationship between $\log k_{obs}$ and $-H_0$ with unit slope.

(b) The reaction is 1000 times faster than that of the 4-pyridyl analogue.

(c) The entropy of activation is small.

Solution. The relationship between k_{obs} and H_0 indicates that the protonated species is undergoing reaction in a monomolecular step (i.e. an *A*-1 mechanism) and protonation will occur on the most basic site, which is the pyridyl nitrogen, to give **2**. The difference in rate for the 4- and 2-pyridyl compounds indicates an intramolecular mechanism for the latter and the size of the entropy of activation is consistent with this. This suggests the following mechanism, where the slow step is intramolecular cyclization and there is protonation of the leaving group.

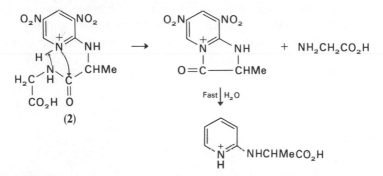

What effect on the rate would replacing H_2O by D_2O have? A. Signor and E. Bordignon, *J. Org. Chem.*, **30**, 3447 (1965).

85. Hydrolysis of 4-(2′-acetoxyphenyl)imidazole (**1**) was thought to occur by a slow acyl transfer to nitrogen and subsequent rapid attack by water as follows.

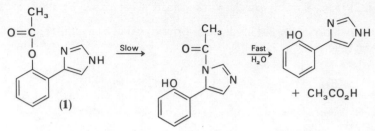

Discuss this mechanism in the light of the following new evidence and suggest a more probable one.

(a) The reaction is 2·3 times faster in H_2O than D_2O.

(b) The entropy of activation has a large negative value.

(c) Esters react with hydrazine

e.g. $CH_3CO_2Ph + NH_2NH_2 \rightarrow CH_3CONHNH_2 + PhOH$

and the kinetic equation has the form:

$$\text{Rate} = k_n(\text{Ester})(NH_2NH_2) + k_{gb}(\text{Ester})(NH_2NH_2)^2$$

i.e. attack of hydrazine is assisted by a second molecule of hydrazine. In the reaction of **1** with hydrazine the term first order in hydrazine (k_n) is larger than anticipated, but there is no term which is second order in hydrazine.

Solution. The reduction in rate in going from H_2O to D_2O indicates involvement of water in the rate-determining step, which is not the case in the scheme shown above. Also the cyclic transition would give rise to a small entropy of activation, which was not observed experimentally. Therefore, water must be present in the transition state and the results may be explained by intramolecular general-base catalysed attack of water.

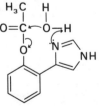

In the reaction with hydrazine, the imidazole replaces the second hydrazine molecule in assisting attack and, thus, there is no term which is second order in hydrazine. S. M. Felton and T. C. Bruice, *Chem. Commun.*, **1968**, 907.

86. 2-Chloro- and 2-bromo-4,4-diphenylcyclohexanones undergo the Favorskii rearrangement in the presence of methoxide. According to R. B. Loftfield [*J. Amer. Chem. Soc.*, **73**, 4707 (1951)] the mechanism of the Favorskii rearrangement is slow removal of a proton followed by rapid expulsion of halide ion via formation of a cyclopropane derivative.

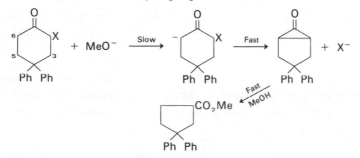

Discuss this mechanism in the light of the following experimental observations.

(a) The bromo compound reacts 116 times faster than the chloro.

(b) With the chloro compound there is no change in rate on replacing protium by deuterium at the 6-position.

(c) With the bromo compound similar isotopic replacement reduces the rate by a factor of four.

Solution. The large difference in rate between the chloro and bromo compounds suggests different mechanisms. The isotope effect for the bromo compound is consistent with the Loftfield mechanism (i.e. slow proton or deuteron removal). The absence of an isotope effect with the chloro compound may be explained by assuming that the second step is slow and this is preceded by a rapid, equilibrium ionization to give the anion. Thus, all the deuterium is lost and replaced by protium on solution and there is no change in the rate of reaction. F. G. Bordwell, R. R. Frame, R. G. Scamehorm, J. G. Strong, and S. Meyerson, *J. Amer. Chem. Soc.*, **89**, 6704 (1967).

87*. The Beckmann rearrangement of the oxime of 2,4,6-trimethylacetophenone to *N*-2,4,6-trimethylphenylacetamide in perchloric acid has been studied, with the following results.

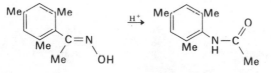

(a) There is spectroscopic evidence for formation of an intermediate, the life-time of which increases with increasing acidity.

(b) The rate of formation of the intermediate was found to be proportional to H_0.

(c) Studies of the rearrangement in perchloric acid enriched with ^{18}O showed there was no incorporation of ^{18}O in unreacted oxime but the acetamide obtained was enriched with ^{18}O.

Solution. As formation of the intermediate is acid-catalysed it must be formed from a protonated form of the oxime. Protonation on the oxygen gives a species which can lose water as the leaving group. Appearance of ^{18}O in the product from enriched water shows that the oxygen of the amide is not that in the original oxime and the absence of ^{18}O in unreacted oxime means that breaking of the nitrogen–oxygen bond is an irreversible step. These conclusions lead to the following possible mechanism.

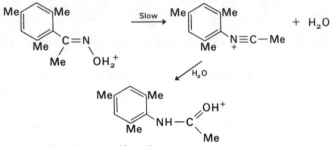

Another possible intermediate is

and the authors distinguish these possibilities by n.m.r. data. B. J. Gregory, R. B. Moodie, and K. Schofield, *J. Chem. Soc. (B)*, **1970**, 338.

88. Benzenediazonium tetrafluoroborate decomposes in dimethyl sulphoxide with evolution of nitrogen and phenylation of any aromatic present. The following isomer ratios were obtained for the phenylation of toluene, chlorobenzene, and nitrobenzene.

	%o	%m	%p
$PhCH_3$	47·3	21·1	31·6
PhCl	48	24·0	27·8
$PhNO_2$	38·1	48·4	13·5

The rates of reaction correlate with σ^+ and the value of ρ is -0.74. The isomer ratios are the same for anisole-d_4 and anisole. Is phenylation under these conditions free radical or electrophilic and what is the rate-determining step?

Solution. In this reaction the nitro group is mainly *m*-directing, while methyl and chloro give mostly *o*- and *p*-isomers. This suggests that the reaction is electrophilic attack with low selectivity, much lower than that for nitration and halogenation. Correlation with σ^+ and the sign of ρ agrees with this. The experiment with anisole-d_4 shows that attack by the phenyl cation, rather than loss of a proton, is the slow step. M. Kobayashi, H. Minato, E. Yamada, and N. Kobori, *Bull. Chem. Soc. Japan*, **43**, 215 (1970).

89. Thermal decarboxylation of 2,2-dimethyl-4-phenylbut-3-enoic acid gives 2-methyl-4-phenylbut-2-ene and carbon dioxide.

$$PhCH{=}CH{-}CMe_2CO_2H \rightarrow PhCH_2{-}CH{=}CMe_2 + CO_2$$

$$\begin{array}{ccc} \uparrow & \uparrow & \uparrow \\ c & b & a \end{array}$$

Substitution of protium by deuterium at position a gives an observed isotope effect (k_H/k_D) of 2·87. *Also*, there is a carbon isotope effect (k_{12}/k_{14}) at position b of 1·035. (This is large for a carbon isotope effect.)

Show how these observations indicate a 'concerted' mechanism for the decarboxylation reaction and suggest a possible transition state.

Solution. In general a reaction displays a primary isotope effect if the bond to the atom under consideration is weakened in the transition state of the rate-determining step. Therefore, in this reaction the bonds to H_a and C_b must both be breaking in the slow step. In most cases the breaking of one bond constitutes the slow process and the observation of two isotope effects indicates a 'concerted' or 'no mechanism' reaction. This, and the

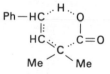

shift in the double bond, suggests a cyclic transition state. D. B. Bigley and J. C. Thurman, *J. Chem. Soc. (B)*, **1967**, 941.

Would you expect any change in rate on replacing the protium at position c by deuterium?

90. Explain the observation that electrophilic hydroxylation at 4-deuterio-acetanilide by trifluoroperacetic acid leads to 4-hydroxyacetanilide, 7·5%

of which contains deuterium in the 3-position.

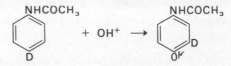

Solution. This is known as the NIH (National Institutes of Health) shift after the place of its discovery. The proposed mechanism is as follows:

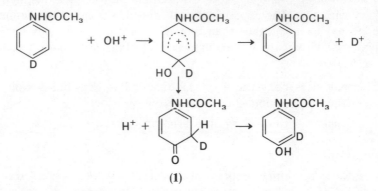

(1)

This migration occurs owing to the stabilization of the diene structure (**1**). The NIH shift has been shown to occur during enzymatic hydroxylation. D. Jerina, J. Daly, W. Landis, B. Witkop, and S. Udenfriend, *J. Amer. Chem. Soc.*, **89**, 3347 (1967).

91. Nitration of aniline in sulphuric acid in the range 89·4–98% gives, as the main products, a mixture of *p*- and *m*-nitroaniline and it was thought that the two products arose from nitration of the free and protonated amine respectively. Examine this hypothesis in the light of the following new experimental results showing the variation of *meta/para* ratio with increasing acidity.

$[H_2SO_4]$ M	89·4	92·4	94·8	96·4	98·0
$10^{-9}h_0$	0·68	2·34	7·41	13·2	25·7
meta %	45	53	57	58	62
para %	52	47	43	42	38

It was also found that the nitration of the phenyltrimethylammonium ion shows the same variation in rate with acidity as that of aniline. Assume that aniline ($pK_a = 4.58$) acts as a normal Hammett base.

Solution. From the pK_a of aniline and the h_0 values it is clear that aniline is completely protonated in 89·4% acid for aniline is half neutralized even at its pK_a [i.e. $(H^+) = 2.63 \times 10^{-3}$ M] and h_0 is a measure of (H^+) in concentrated acid. However, the *p*-isomer could arise from the facile nitration of unprotonated aniline even if present at very low concentration. In going from 89·4 to 98·0% acid there is a large increase in acidity, with a consequent decrease in the concentration of unprotonated aniline but the m/p ratio changes only slightly. Therefore, p-nitroaniline cannot arise from nitration of unprotonated aniline. The authors conclude that the mechanism is attack of NO_2^+ on protonated aniline and that the $-NH_3^+$ group is m/p-directing. This is confirmed by comparison with nitration of the phenyltrimethylammonium ion when reaction must, necessarily, involve the charged substrate. M. Brickman and J. H. Ridd, *J. Chem. Soc.*, **1965**, 6845.

92. Ammonia reacts with phenyl esters to give amides.

$$NH_3 + XC_6H_4OCOCH_3 \rightarrow NH_2COCH_3 + XC_6H_4OH$$

In the presence of an excess of ammonia the kinetic equation is as follows:

$$\text{Rate} = k_{obs}[\text{Ester}]$$

Ammonolysis is subject to catalysis by any base present,

$$k_{obs} = k_1[NH_3] + k_2[NH_3]^2 + k_3[NH_3][OH^-]$$

The following results were obtained for the variation of k_{obs} with pH for two substituted phenyl acetates.

p-CH$_3$C$_6$H$_4$OCOCH$_3$			p-NO$_2$C$_6$H$_4$OCOCH$_3$		
pH	[NH$_3$]M	$10^2 k_{obs}$ min^{-1}	pH	[NH$_3$]M	$10^2 k_{obs}$ min^{-1}
8·38	0·058	0·90	8·24	0·0053	15·8
9·05	0·152	3·17	8·60	0·0113	32·9
9·31	0·234	6·05	8·75	0·0062	17·3
9·45	0·376	12·25	9·00	0·0239	70·3
9·71	0·369	11·13	9·15	0·0127	37·4
9·80	0·532	20·50	9·68	0·0605	168·4

[NH$_3$] indicates the concentration of free (i.e. unprotonated) ammonia at that pH.

(a) Show that, for these two esters, there is no specific base-catalysis.

(b) Determine the values of k_1 and k_2 for both esters and comment on them.

Solution. If k_3 is zero (i.e. no specific base-catalysis) then a plot of $k_{obs}/[NH_3]$ versus [NH$_3$] should be linear with an intercept of k_1 and a slope of k_2. The values obtained for p-methylphenyl acetate are 0·13 l mol^{-1} min^{-1} and 0.54 l^2 mol^2 min^{-1} and, although the pH changes, the graph is still linear. For as poor a leaving group as the p-methylphenoxy anion, assisted ammonolysis is clearly an important pathway.

For the p-nitro ester $k_{obs}/[NH_3]$ is constant and independent of the pH. Therefore, k_2 is zero and k_1 is 29·1 l mol^{-1} min^{-1}. With such a good leaving group as *p*-nitrophenoxy, there is no assisted reaction or, at least, it is too small to detect. T. C. Bruice and M. F. Mayahi, *J. Amer. Chem. Soc.*, **82**, 3067 (1960).

93*. Acid-catalysed decarboxylation is a fairly facile reaction (see Hine, pp. 309–310) and has been extensively studied in the case of azulene-1-carboxylic acid.

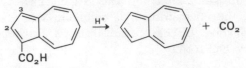

The rate of decarboxylation in perchloric acid of varying concentration has been examined and three distinct regions were found : (i) 0·0001 to 0·30 M : rate is directly proportional to acid concentration, (ii) 0·30 to 6 M : rate is constant and *independent* of the acid concentration, and (iii) 6 M and above : rate decreases with increasing acidity.

These results suggest changes of mechanism with acidity. From the following observations suggest what these changes are :

(a) The u.v. spectrum of the acid is unaffected by addition of perchloric acid up to 6 M.

(b) In 0·01 M acid the rate changes by a factor (k_H/k_D) of 2·15 on moving from $HClO_4$ to $DClO_4$.

(c) In 0·5 M acid the k_H/k_D ratio is only 1·17.

(d) In 0·01 M acid azulenecarboxylic acid with ^{13}C in the carboxylic group reacts at the same rate as that with ^{12}C (i.e. $k_{12}/k_{13} = 1$).

(e) In 0·5 M acid $k_{12}/k_{13} = 1·04$ (this is large for a carbon isotope effect).

(f) Above 6 M acid a new peak at 4 p.p.m. in the n.m.r. of the ring protons appears.

Solution. As the reaction is acid-catalysed, protonation of the carboxylic acid must occur. The most likely site for this is the carbonyl group but this cannot be the case as the u.v. spectrum is unaffected by perchloric acid : therefore, ring protonation must occur, probably at position 1. Protonation can occur either as a slow step or in an equilibrium, and a change from one to the other explains the observed results. Let us assume the following reaction scheme.

$$AzCO_2H + H^+ \underset{k_1}{\overset{k_1}{\rightleftharpoons}} AzH^+CO_2H$$

$$AzH^+CO_2H \overset{k_2}{\rightarrow} AzH^+CO_2^- + H^+$$

$$AzH^+CO_2^- \overset{k_3}{\rightarrow} AzH + CO_2$$

If k_3 is the slow step the kinetic equation is as follows.

$$\text{Rate} = k_3[\text{AzH}^+\text{CO}_2^-]$$

A C—C bond is broken in the rate-determining step.

Now $[\text{AzH}^+\text{Co}_2^-]$ is independent of the acid concentration as acid will increase the concentration of $\text{AzH}^+\text{CO}_2\text{H}$ but suppress its ionization. Therefore, in the acid range 0·30 to 6 M, the rate of reaction is independent of the acid concentration. At very low acid concentration the slow step is k_1 and the rate is directly proportional to the acid concentration. This change in rate-determining step is consistent with the observed isotope effects as there is a change in rate only if the appropriate bond is broken in the rate-determining step. In 6 M acid there is protonation at the $C_{(3)}$ position. J. M. Los, R. F. Rekker, and C. H. T. Tonsbeek, *Rec. Trav. Chim.*, **86**, 622 (1967). J. L. Longridge and F. A. Long, *J. Amer. Chem. Soc.*, **90**, 3092 (1968). H. H. Huang and F. A. Long, *J. Amer. Chem. Soc.*, **91**, 2872 (1969).

Why can the result not be explained by assuming complete protonation at $C_{(1)}$ in 0·3 M acid and slow decarboxylation of the species $\text{AzH}^+\text{CO}_2\text{H}$? What effect would electron-withdrawing substituents in the seven-membered ring have upon the rate of decarboxylation?

94. The reaction of *o*-xylene and nitric acid in acetic anhydride results in acetoxylation as well as nitration.

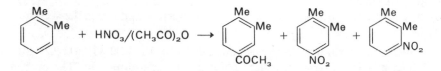

From the following observations suggest the species responsible for nitration and acetoxylation and specify the rate-determining step in the reaction.

(a) Variation in the nitric acid concentration has a considerable effect on the rate of the overall reaction but the ratio of nitration to acetoxylation remains unchanged at 0·71.

(b) Nitric acid and acetic anhydride react, in an equilibrium process, to form acetyl nitrate.

$$(\text{CH}_3\text{CO})_2\text{O} + \text{HNO}_3 \rightleftharpoons \text{CH}_3\text{CONO}_3 + \text{CH}_3\text{CO}_2\text{H}$$

(c) The rates of nitration and acetoxylation are accelerated equally by addition of sulphuric acid.

(d) At high concentrations of *o*-xylene the reaction is zero order in *o*-xylene and *m*-xylene reacts at the same rate.

Solution. As the ratio of nitration to acetoxylation is independent of the nitric acid concentration, the same species must be responsible for both reactions. The known presence of acetyl nitrate makes this a likely species, but the catalytic effect of sulphuric acid means it must react in its protonated form. As the reaction rate is independent of the concentration of the aromatic compound, the rate-determining step must be a slow proton transfer to give protonated acetyl nitrate, which then reacts in a fast step with the aromatic compound. The rate-determining step cannot occur before protonation, otherwise the reaction would not be acid-catalysed. A. Fischer, J. Packer, J. Vaughan, and G. J. Wright, *J. Chem. Soc.*, **1964**, 3687.

[A rate-determining proton transfer to give an electrophilic species is a reaction without precedent and since the publication of the above paper, the authors have somewhat modified their interpretation (D. J. Blackstock, A. Fischer, K. E. Richards, J. Vaughan, and G. J. Wright, *Chem. Commun.*, **1970**, 641) in terms of an addition–elimination mechanism.]

95. Ethyl vinyl ether is readily hydrolysed in dilute acid.

$$EtOCH=CH_2 + H_2O \rightarrow EtOH + CH_3CHO$$

Suggest a mechanism consistent with the following observations, paying particular attention to the position of protonation.

(a) The reaction is subject to general acid-catalysis.

(b) The reaction is faster in H_2O than in D_2O by a factor of 2·93.

(c) The ethanol obtained by hydrolysis in isotopically labelled water contains no ^{18}O.

(d) If hydrolysis occurs in D_2O only *one* deuterium appears in the acetaldehyde.

Solution. General acid-catalysis and the size of the $k(H_2O)/k(D_2O)$ ratio indicate a slow proton transfer as the rate-determining step. The proton will add to the CH_2 group, giving the following carbonium ion.

$$EtO-CH=CH_2 + HA \xrightarrow{Slow} EtO-\overset{+}{C}H-CH_3 + A^-$$

Subsequent reaction with water, a fast step, must involve fission of the C—OEt bond and not alkyl–oxygen fission as no ^{18}O appears in the ethanol. The appearance of only one deuterium in acetaldehyde indicates that protonation cannot be an equilibrium process as this would lead to replacement of H by D in the vinyl ether and, after attack of D_2O, would give acetaldehyde containing more than one deuterium. A. J. Kresge and Y. Chiang, *J. Chem. Soc.* (*B*), **1967**, 53.

96. Hydrazobenzene rearranges in acid solution to give mainly benzidine

Discuss the mechanism given the following experimental observations.

(a) The kinetic equation for the reaction is

$$\text{Rate} = k_{obs}[\text{Hydrazobenzene}]$$

(b) In aqueous dioxan k_{obs} varies with acid concentration in the following way.

$[HClO_4]$ M	0·198	0·297	0·343	0·435	0·540	0·640
H_0	1·565	1·363	1·295	1·175	1·068	0·985
$10^3 k_{obs}$ sec^{-1}	1·14	3·10	4·75	6·70	11·9	22·0

(Note particularly the slope of a plot of $\log k_{obs}$ versus $-H_0$.)

(c) On changing the solvent from 60% dioxan–H_2O to 60% dioxan–D_2O the rate increases by a factor of 4·8.

(d) There is a strong, positive salt effect.

(e) Substitution of deuterium at the p-position has no effect on either the rate of reaction or the products.

(f) Addition of radical scavengers has no effect on the rate or the products.

Solution. From (f) the reaction cannot be a free-radical one. A plot of $\log k_{obs}$ against $-H_0$ has a slope of about two, indicating a kinetic equation of the form

$$\text{Rate} = k[\text{Hydrazobenzene}]h_0^2$$

with a diprotonated species in the transition state. This highly charged species is consistent with a large salt effect. The increase in rate on replacing H_2O by D_2O indicates that the protonated species must be formed in an equilibrium process preceding the rate-determining step (specific acid-catalysis).

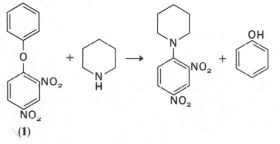

The slow step is probably fission of the N—N bond as isotopic substitution at the p-positions has no effect on the rate. D. V. Banthorpe, E. D. Hughes, C. K. Ingold, and J. Roy, *J. Chem. Soc.*, **1962**, 3294.

97*. Nucleophilic attack of piperidine on 2,4-dinitrodiphenyl ether (1) results in the following reaction.

From the following observations suggest a detailed mechanism of reaction, indicating the rate-determining step in each case.

(a) From **1** or from 2,4-dinitro-4'-methoxydiphenyl ether (**2**) the only phenolic products are phenol and *p*-methoxyphenol, respectively.

(b) With **1** and **2** the kinetic equation is:

$$\text{Rate} = k_n[\text{Ether}][\text{Piperidine}] + k_{\text{OH}^-}[\text{Ether}][\text{Piperidine}][\text{OH}^-]$$

where k_n is the rate constant for nucleophilic attack and k_{OH^-} that for hydroxide-catalysed nucleophilic attack.

(c) For 2,2',4,4'-tetranitrodiphenyl ether there is no third-order term.

(d) The rate of reaction of **1** at constant piperidine concentration becomes independent of $[\text{OH}^-]$ at high pH, and the same effect is observed for **2** but at a higher pH.

(e) For the reaction of **1** with piperidine, catalysed by OH^-, molecules with ^{16}O as the ether oxygen react more rapidly than those with ^{18}O. At 0·005 M hydroxide ion concentration the ratio of rate constants k_{16}/k_{18} is 1·0109. However, at higher pH's the ratio approaches unity.

Solution. From the products of reaction attack of piperidine is on the ring carrying the two nitro groups. The overall mechanism is that common to all cases of nucleophilic aromatic substitution.

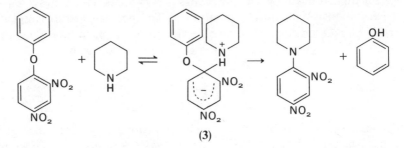

(3)

With poor leaving groups the breakdown of the intermediate **3** is catalysed by OH^- but with a good leaving group (2,4-dinitrophenoxy) this does not occur. At low pH OH^--catalysed breakdown of **3** is slower than attack of piperidine on the ether and the rate of reaction increases with increasing pH. At a certain pH, however, the second step becomes so fast that it is no longer rate-determining and, from then on, the rate of reaction is independent of pH. With a very poor leaving group (*p*-methoxyphenoxy) this will only occur at a very high pH. At low pH the rate-determining step involves fission of a C—O bond and will, therefore, display an oxygen isotope effect. At high pH the rate-determining step changes to one in which the C—O bond is not broken and there is no isotope effect. J. F.

Bunnett and C. Bernasconi, *J. Amer. Chem. Soc.*, **87**, 5209 (1965). C. R. Hart and A. N. Bourns, *Tetrahedron Letters*, **1966**, 2995.

98. Aromatic compounds may be brominated by an acidified solution of hypobromous acid in 75% aqueous acetic acid. The following results were obtained.

(a) For the bromination of benzene and biphenyl

$$\text{Rate} = k[\text{ArH}][\text{BrOH}]$$

(b) The following figures were obtained for the variation of k with h_0 for the bromination of biphenyl at $0.86°$.

$[\text{HClO}_4]$ M	0.0053	0.0106	0.0212	0.0267
$k\,l\,\text{mol}^{-1}\,\text{sec}^{-1}$	5.8	7.4	9.7	12.2
$10^3 h_0$	8.0	12.3	23.0	29.5

(c) Diphenyl reacts faster than benzene.

(d) For the reaction of diphenyl the $\frac{1}{2}o/p$ ratio varies with acidity, being 0.17 in the absence of acid and reaching a limiting value of 0.59 at 0.2 M acid. Explain these observations in terms of two different brominating species.

Solution. As biphenyl reacts more rapidly than benzene the attacking species must be electrophilic as the phenyl group is activating towards electrophiles, and the detection of acid-catalysis suggests that the species is protonated. However, there is a positive intercept of ca. 3.3 in a plot of k against h_0, so there must also be a non-catalysed reaction. A possible brominating species in this case is bromine acetate, giving an $\frac{1}{2}o/p$ ratio of 0.17. With increasing acid concentration the acid-catalysed reaction becomes the dominant one, with an $\frac{1}{2}o/p$ ratio of 0.59. The attacking species in this case is probably BrOH_2^+ (i.e. protonated hypobromous acid)

$$\text{BrOH}_2^+ \rightleftharpoons \text{Br}^+ + \text{H}_2\text{O}$$

or Br^+, species which are in equilibrium. P. B. D. de la Mare and J. L. Maxwell, *J. Chem. Soc.*, **1962**, 4829.

99. In acetic acid solution *o*-nitrobenzhydryl bromide (**1**) decomposes spontaneously in two ways: in the presence of an excess of HBr the sole product is 5-bromo-3-phenyl-2,1-benisoxazole (**2**) but in the presence of sodium acetate (which removes any HBr formed) the product is *o*-nitroso-benzophenone (**3**).

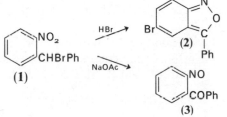

First order rate constants for these reactions are as follows:

[NaOAc]M	[HBr]M	$10^5 k \, sec^{-1}$	Product
0·02	—	9·0	3
0·05	—	9·5	3
—	0·01	8·4	2
—	0·1	9·4	2

In the absence of either HBr or sodium acetate the final product is a mixture of **2** and **3** with **2** predominating. Compound **2** forms only after an induction period.

p-Nitrobenzyhydryl bromide reacts with acetic acid in the presence of sodium acetate. The first order rate constant for this reaction is $3·12 \times 10^{-8}$ sec^{-1}.

Suggest a mechanism for the formation of **2** and **3**.

Solution. The enhanced rate of reaction of the *ortho* compound, compared to the *para*, indicates that the nitro group is participating in the reaction. The other significant observation is that the rate is independent of the product and the amount of HBr or sodium acetate present. This suggests that either (a) the slow step is formation of a common intermediate which decomposes to give either **2** or **3**, or (b) the slow step is formation of **3** which, in the presence of HBr, is rapidly converted into **2**. A possible intermediate,

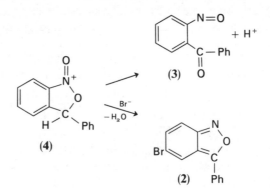

suggested by the authors, is **4** which either loses a proton to give **3** or undergoes nucleophilic attack by bromide at the 5-position with subsequent dehydration to give **2**.

In the absence of any additive **3** is the only product until enough HBr has collected to convert it, or the common intermediate, into **2**. S. Kim, S. S. Friedrich, L. J. Andrews, and R. M. Keefer, *J. Amer. Chem. Soc.*, **92**, 5452 (1970).

The authors tacitly reject mechanism (b) above. Do you think they are justified in doing so? There are data concerning conversion of **3** into **2** in the experimental section of the paper.

100. Substituted methyl benzoates hydrolyse rapidly in 95 % sulphuric acid. A study of the effect of substituents in the phenyl ring on the rate of reaction gave the following results.

Substituent	p-Me	m-Me	H	m-Cl	m-Br
$10^4 k$ sec^{-1}	2·41	1·51	0·65	0·035	0·032

Determine the value of ρ for this reaction and predict the rate constant for the hydrolysis of methyl p-fluorobenzoate.

For the hydrolysis of methyl o-methylbenzoate and methyl p-methoxybenzoate the rate constants are 182×10^{-4} sec^{-1} and $10\cdot2 \times 10^{-4}$ sec^{-1}, respectively. Comment on these results.

Substituents have very little effect upon the rate of hydrolysis of methyl benzoates in *dilute* sulphuric acid. Compare this observation with the results given above and suggest an explanation. (Values of σ can be found on p. 10.)

Solution. A plot of log k/k_0 versus σ is linear and the slope of this line (i.e. ρ) is $-3\cdot4$. From the known value of σ for fluorine the ratio $k_F/k_0 = 0\cdot62$ and this gives $k_F = 4\cdot0 \times 10^{-5}$ sec^{-1}.

The value for methyl o-methylbenzoate is much greater than that of the m- or p-isomers showing that, as expected for an o-substituent, it does not fit a simple Hammett $\sigma\rho$ plot. There is no obvious reason why the p-methoxy compound should not lie on the line obtained for the other compounds, but, by using the value of σ_p for methoxy, the rate is found to be enhanced.

Hydrolysis in concentrated sulphuric acid involves formation of a carbonium ion (**1**)

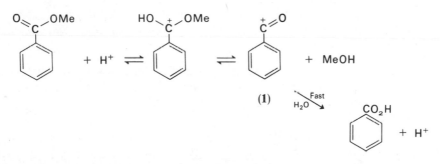

and substitution will greatly affect the ease with which **1** forms. In dilute acid, however, the slow step is attack of water on the protonated ester:

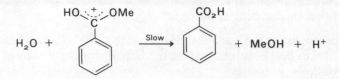

and this reaction is much less sensitive to substituents.

The enhanced rate for the *p*-methoxy compound is not easy to under-stand, but the system must gain some conjugative energy in going from the protonated ester to the transition state for hydrolysis. With the *o*-methyl compound steric strain will be lost on going to the transition state as it is less space-demanding than the protonated ester, leading to an enhanced rate of reaction. H. van Bekkum, H. M. A. Buurmans, B. M. Wepster, and A. M. van Wijk, *Rec. Trav. Chim.*, **88**, 301 (1969). E. W. Timm and C. N. Hinshelwood, *J. Chem. Soc.*, **1938**, 862.

101. *p*-Chlorobenzaldehyde undergoes the normal reaction with semi-carbazide to give a semicarbazone, and the reaction is subject to general acid-catalysis.

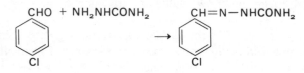

In a study of aniline as a catalyst several unexpected results were obtained.

(a) It is much more effective as a catalyst than its pK_a value would indicate.

(b) The rate of the aniline-catalysed reaction is independent of the semi-carbazide concentration and is the same as the aniline-catalysed formation of the corresponding oxime (reaction with hydroxylamine).

(c) The Schiff's base formed between aniline and *p*-chlorobenzaldehyde reacts rapidly with semicarbazide to give the semicarbazone. How may this result be explained?

Solution. Aniline must be acting as a nucleophilic catalyst rather than a general acid/base catalyst. The rate-determining step is formation of the Schiff's base from aniline and *p*-chlorobenzaldehyde:

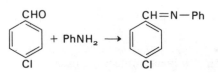

and this reacts with semicarbazide in a fast step. The rate is, therefore, independent of the semicarbazide concentration. Aniline-catalysed oxime formation has the same rate-determining step and so the overall rate is the same. E. H. Cordes and W. P. Jencks, *J. Amer. Chem. Soc.*, **84**, 826 (1962).

102. *p*-Chlorobenzonitrile-*N*-oxide (**1**) reacts with an excess of phenylacetylene (**2**) to give a mixture of 3-(*p*-chlorophenyl)-5-phenylisoxazole (**3**) and 1-*p*-chlorophenyl-3-phenylprop-2-ynone oxime (**4**). It is known that **4** will

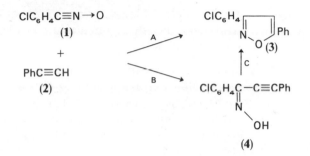

cyclize to give **3** (route C). The formation of the isoxazole **3** could occur either by a concerted process (route A) and/or by formation of the oxime **4** and subsequent cyclization to **3** (routes B and C).

The ratio of **3** to **4** present, and the rate constants for their formation, were determined at various stages during the course of a reaction, with the following results.

Reaction (%)	Ratio 3/4	$10^3 k_3$ l mol^{-1} sec^{-1}	$10^3 k_4$ l mol^{-1} sec^{-1}
19·9	2·30	9·01	4·11
35·1	2·38	9·07	3·81
54·3	2·28	8·51	3·74
67·3	2·57	9·24	3·59
79·3	2·36	8·46	3·80

Which mechanism do these results indicate?

Solution. The constancy of the ratio **3/4** throughout the reaction (= 2·40) shows that cyclization of **4** cannot be an important pathway in the formation of the oxazole **3**. If it were, then C would be the slow step and there would be a gradual build up of **4** as the reaction proceeded. Further confirmation comes from the fact that the ratio of the rate constants for the formation of the products (k_3/k_4) is the same (= 2·38) as their relative occurrence in the product. A. Battaglia, A. Dondoni, and A. Mangini, *J. Chem. Soc. (B)*, **1971**, 554.

103. A study has been made of the acid-catalysed hydrolysis of a number of cyclic carbonates.

$$(CH_2)_n \quad C=O + H_2O \longrightarrow (CH_2)_n \quad + CO_2$$

(with OH and OH groups shown on product, and O, O on the carbonate)

(a) For 2,2-diethyltrimethylene carbonate the reaction is faster in D_2O than H_2O.

(b) For propylene carbonate a plot of log k_{obs} versus H_0 is not linear.

(c) For trimethylene carbonate the entropy of activation is $-31\cdot6$ e.u.

Suggest a mechanism for this reaction.

Solution. The faster rate in D_2O means there must be an equilibrium protonation preceding the rate-determining step (D_2O is a weaker base than H_2O so there must be a higher concentration of protonated substrate in D_2O than H_2O). The lack of linear dependence on H_0 means that the reaction is not A-1 and the size of $\Delta S^{\ddagger}$ is consistent with an A-2 mechanism.

If S is the cyclic carbonate

$$S + H^+ \rightleftharpoons SH^+$$

$$SH^+ + H_2O \xrightarrow{\text{Slow}} HO(CH_2)_nOCO_2H + H^+$$

$$HO(CH_2)_nOCO_2H \xrightarrow{\text{Fast}} HO(CH_2)_nOH + CO_2$$

I. Levin, L. A. Pohoryles, S. Sarel, and V. Usieli, *J. Chem. Soc.*, **1963**, 3949.

104. *N*-Chlorosuccinimide (NCS) will oxidize isopropyl alcohol to acetone and the rate of reaction has been studied by measuring the amount of NCS remaining at timed intervals. The following results were obtained.

(a) The reaction is catalysed by acid.

(b) There is an induction period of five to ten minutes and after that the rate is first order in NCS.

(c) The reaction is zero order in isopropyl alcohol and oxidation of other alcohols occurs at the same rate.

(d) The rate is increased by addition of chloride ion and the induction period is removed.

Suggest a mechanism for oxidation, indicating which is the rate-determining step.

Solution. The above observations indicate that the rate-determining step must consist of an acid-catalysed reaction between chloride ion and NCS, and this is followed by rapid reaction with alcohol. Chlorine will oxidize alcohols, so the essential part of the reaction is production of free chlorine.

$$\begin{array}{c}CH_2CO \\ | \quad\quad\quad >NCl + H^+ \\ CH_2CO\end{array} \rightleftharpoons \begin{array}{c}CH_2CO \\ | \quad\quad\quad >NHCl^+ \\ CH_2CO\end{array}$$

$$\begin{array}{c}CH_2CO \\ | \quad\quad\quad >NHCl^+ + Cl^- \\ CH_2CO\end{array} \rightarrow \begin{array}{c}CH_2CO \\ | \quad\quad\quad >NH + Cl_2 \\ CH_2CO\end{array}$$

$$PrOH + Cl_2 \xrightarrow{\text{Fast}} Products$$

In the absence of chloride ion there is no reaction, but this ion is probably slowly produced spontaneously by decomposition of NCS, which explains the induction period. As reaction with alcohol comes after the rate-determining step, there is zero-order dependence on the alcohol concentration. N. D. Srinivasan and N. Venkatasubramanian, *Tetrahedron Letters*, **1970**, 2039.

If *N*-bromosuccinimide is used the reaction is first order in alcohol. What does this indicate?

105*. Spectral studies show that, in acid solution, phenylbenzoylacetylene (**1**) is protonated to a certain extent on the oxygen of the carbonyl group (**2**).

$$PhC{\equiv}C{-}\overset{\overset{\textstyle O}{\|}}{C}{-}Ph + H_3O^+ \rightleftharpoons PhC{\equiv}C{-}\overset{\overset{\textstyle OH^+}{\|}}{C}{-}Ph + H_2O$$

$$\text{(1)} \quad\quad\quad\quad\quad\quad \text{(2)}$$

There is also a slow, acid-catalysed, hydrolysis to give dibenzoylmethane (**3**).

$$Ph\overset{\overset{\textstyle O}{\|}}{C}{-}CH_2{-}\overset{\overset{\textstyle O}{\|}}{C}Ph$$

$$\text{(3)}$$

There are two possible mechanisms for this hydrolysis:
  (a) Rate-determining attack of water on the protonated molecule (**2**).
  (b) The protonated species **2** is unreactive and the rate-determining step is a proton transfer to **1** to give the carbonium ion **4**, which reacts rapidly with water to give **3**.

$$PhC^+{=}CH{-}\overset{\overset{\textstyle O}{\|}}{C}{-}Ph$$

$$\text{(4)}$$

Which mechanism is consistent with the following observations?
  (i) The reaction is slower in a deuterated solvent.

(ii) The rate of reaction is very sensitive to substituents in the phenyl ring but less so to those in the benzoyl moiety.

(iii) The reaction was found to be first order in **1** and the first order rate constant (k_{obs}) was found to vary with acidity in the following manner.

$\%H_2SO_4$	$-H_0$	$10^5 k_{obs} \, sec^{-1}$	Fraction protonated (α)
59·98	4·65	1·66	0·01
63·73	5·10	4·57	0·04
67·71	5·65	12·4	0·12
71·52	6·18	29·0	0·32
75·51	6·81	53·0	0·66
79·17	7·41	67·7	0·89

Solution. Protonation of the carbonyl group should be sensitive to substituents in the benzoyl moiety but not in the phenyl ring so that (ii) suggests that the protonated species **2** is not involved. This is confirmed by (i) as formation of **2** should be more extensive in a deuteriated solvent. Also, mechanism (a) demands a linear relationship between $\log k_{obs}$ and $-H_0$, which is not found. However, if allowance is made, as indicated below, for protonation to give an unreactive species, then such a linear relationship is found. As the reaction is first order in **1**

$$\text{Rate} = k_{obs}[\mathbf{1}]_{st}$$

where $[\mathbf{1}]_{st}$ = stoicheiometric concentration of **1**

$$[\mathbf{1}] = [\mathbf{1}]_{st}(1 - \alpha)$$

where $[\mathbf{1}]$ = concentration of unprotonated **1** and α = degree of protonation.

For mechanism (b)

$$\text{Rate} = k(H^+)[\mathbf{1}] = k(H^+)[\mathbf{1}]_{st}(1 - \alpha)$$

$$\therefore \quad k_{obs} = k(H^+)(1 - \alpha)$$

and a plot of $\log[k_{obs}/(1 - \alpha)]$ against $-H_0$ is linear.

Thus all the evidence is in favour of mechanism (b). D. S. Noyce and K. E. De Briun, *J. Amer. Chem. Soc.*, **90**, 372 (1968).

106. In the presence of HCl in acetic acid solution diethyl maleate isomerizes to diethyl fumarate:

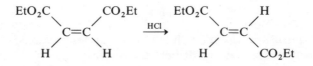

It is, in fact, an equilibrium but lies very much in favour of diethyl fumarate.

Suggest a mechanism in the light of the following experimental observations.

(a) The rate of reaction is unaffected by addition of benzoyl peroxide.

(b) The reaction is first order in both diethyl maleate and HCl.

(c) The reaction is not accelerated by addition of *chloride ion* or *perchloric acid*.

(d) In a mixture of DCl and deuterioacetic acid (CH_3CO_2D) the reaction is faster ($k_H/k_D = 0.5$).

(e) Under the conditions of (d) no deuterium is incorporated into the reactant or product.

Solution. The reaction is clearly not free radical. Catalysis by HCl, but not by perchloric acid or chloride ion, indicates that the reaction is not simple acid-catalysis or nucleophilic attack by chloride ion. Both H^+ and a reasonably strong nucleophile (Cl^-) appear to be necessary for reaction. This result may be explained by 1,4-addition of HCl to a system where the carbonyl group acts as part of the conjugated system of double bonds. This permits free rotation about the central carbon–carbon bond.

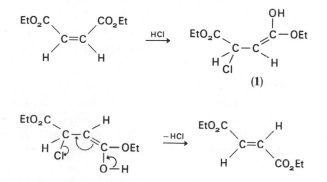

The first step in addition to protonation of the carbonyl group and the rate-determining step is attack by Cl^- to give species **1**. The rate of reaction, therefore, will depend upon the concentration of the protonated species, which will be higher in DCl/AcOD than in the HCl/AcOH. This is because of the conjugate bases, D_2O is weaker than H_2O and thus, in the former medium, deuteriation of diethyl maleate is more extensive. Deuteriation of the carbonyl group, rather than a hydrogen bearing carbon atom, means that elimination of DCl will leave no deuterium incorporated into the reactants or products. R. C. Fahey and H.-J. Schneider, *J. Amer. Chem. Soc.*, **92**, 6885 (1970).

107*. The hydration of phenylacetylene to give acetophenone is catalysed by sulphuric acid:

$$PhC\equiv CH + H_2O \rightarrow PhCOCH_3$$

This reaction could occur by (a) equilibrium protonation of phenylacetylene to give $PhCH=CH^+$ or $PhC^+=CH_2$, followed by slow attack of water or (b) slow proton transfer from an acid to give one of the carbonium ions and subsequent attack by water in a fast process. With which of these mechanisms are the following experimental observations more consistent?

(i) The kinetic equation is

$$Rate = k_{obs}[PhC\equiv CH]$$

and k_{obs} varies with the acidity of the sulphuric acid in the following manner:

$-H_0$	1·82	1·93	2·27	2·36	2·78	3·24
$10^4 k_{obs} \; sec^{-1}$	0·57	0·67	2·06	2·84	8·15	28·8

(Note carefully the slope of the plot of $\log k_{obs}$ against $-H_0$.)

(ii) Catalysis by acetic acid (i.e. general acid-catalysis) was detected in the hydration of *p*-methoxyphenylacetylene in acetate buffer.

(iii) Replacing H_2O by D_2O *reduces* the rate by a factor of two.

(iv) In the hydration of $PhC\equiv CD$ there is no loss of deuterium.

(v) Substituents in the phenyl ring have a very large effect on the rate of reaction.

Solution. A plot of $\log k_{obs}$ against $-H_0$ is linear with a slope that is not unity. This is not in agreement with mechanism (a) as this requires a non-linear plot (Zucker–Hammett hypothesis). This is confirmed by the observation of general acid-catalysis (admittedly not with the unsubstituted compound). Also, retention of deuterium, which would be lost if the $PhC^+=CHD$ ion were formed in an *equilibrium process*, is inconsistent with specific acid-catalysis. The reduction in rate in D_2O indicates that the rate-determining step is transfer of a proton from the acid to phenylacetylene and not an equilibrium protonation and this is consistent with the linear relationship between $\log k_{obs}$ and H_0. The large effect of substituents in the phenyl ring suggests the vinyl cation ($PhC^+=CH_2$) is formed and the positive charge can be delocalized because of its proximity to the phenyl ring, the extent of which will vary with the substituent. D. S. Noyce and M. D. Schiavelli, *J. Amer. Chem. Soc.*, **90**, 1020 (1968).

108. Nucleophilic aromatic substitution does not occur very readily and normally requires the presence of nitro groups attached to the benzene ring to effect reaction. It has been found, however, that 5-chloroacenaphthylene

(1) reacts with ethoxide ion in ethanol to give 5-ethoxyacenaphthylene.

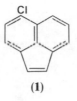

(1)

How may this be explained?

Solution. The electron-withdrawing properties of nitro groups permit nucleophilic aromatic substitution because they delocalize the negative charge, produced by attack of the nucleophile, with formation of a definite intermediate (2).

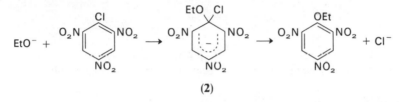

(2)

An analogous intermediate, the cyclopentadienide ion (3), may be formed

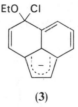

(3)

in this reaction, and thus facilitate nucleophilic substitution. M. J. Perkins, *Chem. Commun.*, **1971**, 231.

109. The rates of hydrolysis of the three related esters have been studied as a function of pH, with the results shown in Figure 7. The entropy of activation

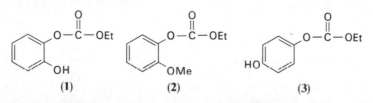

(1)   (2)   (3)

for the hydrolysis of **1** is $-41 \cdot 0$ e.u.

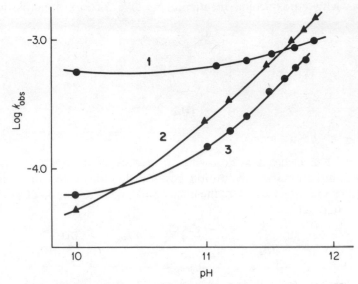

Figure 7. Plot of the rate of hydrolysis of three esters versus pH.

Suggest mechanisms for these reactions.

Solution. The fact that **2** and **3** have similar pH rate profiles with rates which increase as the pH is increased, suggests that the reaction is simple hydrolysis of the carbonate group by hydroxide ion. The elevated rate for **1** at lower pH indicates involvement of the *o*-hydroxy group. The most obvious possibility is rate-determining attack by the ionized hydroxy group on the carbonyl group.

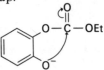

However, this cyclic mechanism should be associated with a small entropy of activation, as it requires very little ordering of the molecules. A more likely mechanism is assisted attack of a water molecule, which should

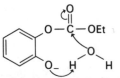

have a negative entropy of activation. J. G. Tillett and D. E. Wiggins, *Tetrahedron Letters*, **1971**, 911.

110. Benzyne is formed by the action of amide ion on a halobenzene in a two-step process.

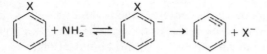

With dihalobenzenes two different benzynes may result depending on which hydrogen is removed and which halogen is expelled. Rationalize the following observations.

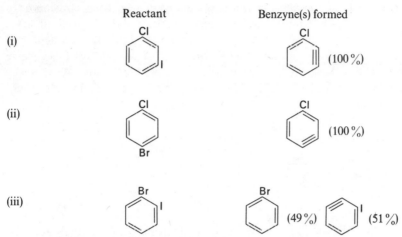

Solution. (i) The hydrogen between the two halogens will be the most acidic, and the benzyne formed will depend only on which halogen is most readily lost. The C—I bond is weaker than the C—Cl bond, so that chlorobenzyne results.

(ii) The anion **1** is formed more readily than **2** (the position *ortho* to a halogen is deactivated towards electrophilic attack and must, therefore, be more susceptible to nucleophilic attack and chlorine has a greater effect than bromine) but reverts mainly to starting material as the C—Cl bond is

strong. The anion **2**, although formed less readily, more easily loses bromine and chlorobenzyne results.

(iii) Proton removal occurs most easily *ortho* to the halogen which is least readily lost and the balance of these two factors gives a 50:50 mixture. J. F. Bunnett and F. J. Kearley, *J. Org. Chem.*, **36**, 184 (1971). (Consultation of the original paper is of entertainment value as well as chemical interest, being written in blank verse. Practising chemists with abilities in the arts are far from uncommon but it would be out of place to mention any by name. Among great figures of the past, Borodin, the Russian composer, started life as a chemist and it is said that Perkin, Jr., was a pianist of outstanding ability.)

111. Hydrolysis of the aspirin anion (**1**) has generally been considered a classic case of rate-determining intramolecular attack of the ionized carboxylate group to give the mixed anhydride of acetic and salicylic acid and subsequent attack by water, but recent work by W. J. Jencks and T. St. Pierre [*J. Amer. Chem. Soc.*, **90**, 3817 (1968)] and A. R. Fersht and A. J. Kirby [*J. Amer. Chem. Soc.*, **89**, 4853, 4857 (1967)] has cast considerable doubt on this mechanism.

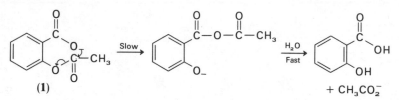

However, the following results were obtained with the dinitro analogue of **1**, which is a much stronger acid.

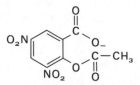

(a) Hydrolysis in water enriched with ^{18}O results in incorporation of ^{18}O in the resulting dinitrosalicylic acid.

(b) In aqueous methanol the major product is methyl 3,5-dinitrosalicylate.

(c) Replacing H_2O by D_2O gives a kinetic isotope effect (k_H/k_D) of 2.0.

(d) The entropy of activation is -20.6 e.u.

Are these results in agreement with the original mechanism proposed for the hydrolysis of aspirin monoanion?

Solution. The ^{18}O can appear in the salicylic acid only if the anhydride is formed as an intermediate: direct attack by water on the acyl group would result in all the ^{18}O appearing in the acetic acid. The formation of methyl 3,5-dinitrosalicylate indicates the same intermediate. However, the kinetic isotope effect and the high negative entropy of activation are both inconsistent with rate-determining intramolecular attack and suggest that the

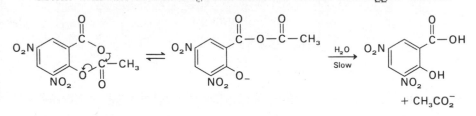

slow step is attack of water on the mixed anhydride. A. R. Fersht and A. J. Kirby, *J. Amer. Chem. Soc.,* **89**, 5960 (1967).

112*. The hydrolysis of *p*-nitrobenzyl chloride in aqueous alkali yields the expected product (*p*-nitrobenzyl alcohol) but with alkali in aqueous dioxan 4,4'-dinitrostilbene (**1**) is obtained.

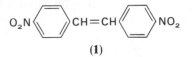

$$O_2N\langle\ \rangle CH{=}CH\langle\ \rangle NO_2$$

(1)

Suggest a mechanism for the latter reaction from the following observations and identify the rate-determining step.

(a) The rate of reaction was measured by monitoring the appearance of chloride ion and the kinetic equation was found to be

$$\text{Rate} = k[ArCH_2Cl][OH^-]$$

(b) Recovery of unreacted *p*-nitrobenzyl chloride after partial reaction in D_2O–dioxan solution showed incorporation of deuterium at the α-position.

(c) In the presence of *p*-nitrobenzaldehyde there was an increase in the rate of production of chloride and an epoxide was obtained as product.

$$NO_2C_6H_4CH\overset{O}{\overbrace{\qquad}}CHPh$$

(d) *p*-Nitrobenzyl chloride deuteriated at the α-position was found to react only 1.28 times slower than the isotopically normal compound.

Solution. The dimerized product and formation of an epoxide from an aldehyde both suggest formation of a carbene. Because deuterium is incorporated into *p*-nitrobenzyl chloride from the solvent, carbene formation must involve an equilibrium and it cannot be rate-determining as appearance of chloride is affected by addition of p-nitrobenzaldehyde. Also proton removal cannot be slow as the rate of reaction is unaffected by deuterium substitution at the α-position. With all these factors in mind the following reaction scheme is possible.

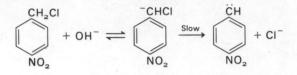

Reaction of the anion with p-nitrobenzaldehyde is faster than loss of chloride to form the carbene. The rate is unaffected by deuteration as there is rapid exchange and most of the deuterium is replaced by protium before loss of chloride. S. H. Hanna, Y. Iskander, and Y. Riad, *J. Chem. Soc.*, **1961**, 217.

What would be the rate of reaction of the deuteriated compound in dioxan–D_2O?

113*. In concentrated sulphuric acid p-hydroxyazobenzene is partially protonated and the protonated and unprotonated forms have absorption maxima at 383 and 323 nm, respectively. The following variation of optical density (D) with acidity was obtained.

%H_2SO_4	$-H_0$	D_{383}	D_{323}
41·07	2·50	0·081	0·904
54·07	3·88	0·127	0·893
64·49	5·01	0·524	0·725
70·16	5·83	0·921	0·518
73·82	6·38	1·015	0·447
77·92	7·01	1·048	0·424
90·49	9·02	1·070	0·392

Using the method of A. R. Katritzky, A. J. Waring, and K. Yates, [*Tetrahedron*, **19**, 465 (1963)] determine the value of the pK_a.

Sulphuric acid also converts p-hydroxyazobenzene into azoxybenzene in a first-order process. From the following data discuss the species undergoing reaction.

%H_2SO_4	$-H_0$	$10^7 k_{obs}$ sec^{-1}
75·30	6·61	1·58
88·22	8·64	524
96·40	10·10	2630

Solution. The pK_a is -5.15 so that, under conditions when conversion to azoxybenzene occurs, p-hydroxyazobenzene is completely protonated and yet the results indicate very pronounced acid-catalysis. Therefore, a diprotonated form must be reacting, probably

$$\overset{\overset{+}{O}H_2^+}{\underset{+}{Ph-N=N-Ph}}$$

The second protonation may be an equilibrium process or a slow proton transfer. E. Buncel and B. T. Lawton, *Canad. J. Chem.*, **43**, 862 (1965) [see also C. S. Hahn, K. W. Lee, and H. H. Jaffé, *J. Amer. Chem. Soc.*, **89**, 4975 (1967)].

114*. The acid-catalysed rearrangement of 1-phenyl-3-methylallyl alcohol to 1-methyl-3-phenylallyl alcohol

$$\underset{\underset{OH}{|}}{PhCHCH=CHMe} \overset{H^+}{\longrightarrow} PhCH=CH-\underset{\underset{OH}{|}}{CHMe}$$

is accompanied by racemization and oxygen exchange. From a kinetic study of these three processes the following data were obtained.

(a) Rearrangement

$10^3[HClO_4]_M$	1·47	2·80	4·74	7·8	8·2	14·7	19·0	23·7
$10^4 k\ sec^{-1}$	1·00	1·98	3·13	5·31	5·73	9·8	13·0	16·2

(b) Racemization of (−)-1-phenyl-3-methylallyl alcohol

$10^3[HClO_4]_M$	1·47	2·80	4·80	7·0	8·4	9·8	10·0	12·0	12·2
$10^4 k\ sec^{-1}$	0·996	1·79	3·40	4·77	6·20	6·56	6·81	8·03	8·57

(c) Exchange of ^{18}O

$10^3[HClO_4]_M$	1·56	3·16	16·7
$10^4 k\ sec^{-1}$	1·06	2·15	11·4

Compare the mechanism of this rearrangement with that of 1-phenylallyl alcohol. H. L. Goering and R. E. Dilgren, *J. Amer. Chem. Soc.*, **81**, 2556 (1959); **82**, 5744 (1960).

Solution. The mechanism of rearrangement of an allylic alcohol is protonation followed by formation of a carbonium ion, and the rearranged product is formed by attack of water on this ion.

$$H^+ + \underset{\underset{OH}{|}}{PhCHCH=CH_2} \overset{1}{\rightleftharpoons} [PhCH\text{⋯}CH\text{⋯}CH_2]^+ + H_2O \overset{2}{\rightleftharpoons} PhCH=CH-\underset{\underset{OH}{|}}{CH_2} + H^+$$

With 1-phenylallyl alcohol racemization and oxygen exchange are faster than rearrangement indicating that there is competition between return and product formation, i.e. step 1 is reversible. Return of the carbonium ion to 1-phenylallyl alcohol results in loss of ^{18}O and racemization but not, of course, in rearrangement. Therefore, the last reaction is slower than the other two. With 3-phenyl-1-methylallyl alcohol all three processes occur at the same rate (with a second order rate constant of 6.8×10^{-2} $l\,mol^{-1}\,sec^{-1}$) indicating that the carbonium ion in this case partitions exclusively in favour of the rearranged product, i.e. step 1 is not reversible. Can you suggest a reason for this? Y. Pocker and M. J. Hill, *J. Amer. Chem. Soc.*, **91**, 3243 (1969).

The authors mention that they hope to study the rearrangement of 1-phenyl-3-(trideuteriomethyl)allyl alcohol. What will this show?

115. Aniline and nitrosobenzene, in the presence of a base, react to give azobenzene.

$$PhNH_2 + PhNO \rightarrow PhN{=}NPh + H_2O$$

From the following observations suggest a mechanism for this reaction.

(a) The rate of reaction is first order in both aniline and nitrosobenzene.

(b) With tetramethylammonium hydroxide as base the rate of reaction was found to be directly proportional to the concentration of base.

(c) With substituents in the phenyl ring of aniline a Hammett plot gave a ρ value of $+2.0$.

(d) For substituents in the nitroso compound the ρ value was -2.1.

Solution. All the observations are consistent with the following scheme:

$$PhNH_2 + OH^- \overset{K}{\rightleftharpoons} PhNH^- + H_2O \tag{1}$$

$$PhNH^- + PhNO \xrightarrow{\text{Slow}} PhNH{-}\overset{\displaystyle O^-}{\underset{\displaystyle |}{N}}Ph \tag{2}$$

$$PhNH{-}\overset{\displaystyle O^-}{\underset{\displaystyle |}{N}}Ph \xrightarrow{\text{Fast}} PhN{=}NPh + OH^- \tag{3}$$

Step (**1**) explains the catalytic effect of the base and also the increase in rate with electron-withdrawing substituents in the aniline (ρ is positive). Attack of this negative species on nitrosobenzene in step (**2**) explains the accelerating effect of electron-donating substituents in the nitrosobenzene (ρ is negative). E. V. Brown and W. H. Kipp, *J. Org. Chem.*, **36**, 170 (1971).

116*. Butenyl magnesium bromide ($1:R = CH_3$), although it is in equilibrium with its crotyl isomer (**2**), reacts with acetone to give exclusively the α-methylallyl carbinol ($3:R = CH_3$) via a non-cyclic S_E2' rearrangement mechanism [H. Felkin, Y. Gault, and G. Roussi, *Tetrahedron*, **26**, 3761 (1970)].

$$\underset{(1)}{\text{R}-\text{CH}=\text{CH}-\overset{\overset{\displaystyle \text{MgBr}}{|}}{\text{CH}_2}} \qquad \underset{(2)}{\text{RCH}_2-\overset{\overset{\displaystyle \text{MgBr}}{|}}{\text{C}}=\text{CH}_2} \qquad \underset{(3)}{\overset{\displaystyle \text{R}-\text{CH}-\text{CH}=\text{CH}_2}{\underset{(\text{CH}_3)_2\text{C}-\text{OH}}{|}}}$$

However, if R = *t*-butyl, the predominant product on reaction with acetone is the γ-*t*-butylallyl carbinol (4).

$$\overset{\displaystyle \text{Bu}^t-\text{CH}=\text{CH}-\text{CH}_2}{\underset{(\text{CH}_3)_2\text{C}-\text{OH}}{|}}$$

(4)

Explain this observation and comment on the fact that the proportion of γ-carbinol is further increased on replacing acetone by hexadeuterioacetone.

Solution. This reaction is a sensitive probe for distinguishing steric and polar effects. The transition states for formation of α- and γ-carbinols are 5 and 6.

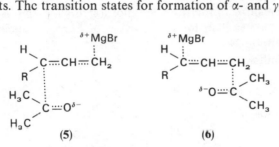

(5)   (6)

If R = Bu^t then steric factors will hinder the formation of 5 and thus favour formation of the γ-carbinol via 6. As the transition states are almost symmetrical the electronic effect of the alkyl group in the ketone is the same in both cases, and the change in going from acetone to hexadeuterioacetone suggests that secondary deuterium isotope effects are steric in origin. M. Cherest, H. Felkin, and C. Frajerman, *Tetrahedron Letters*, **1971**, 379.

117. The hydrolysis of benzenesulphonyl chloride is catalysed by pyridines. The kinetic equation is

$$\text{Rate} = k_{obs}[\text{Benzenesulphonyl chloride}]$$

and

$$k_{obs} = k_0 + k_b[\text{Py}]$$

where k_0 is the rate constant for spontaneous hydrolysis and k_b that for the pyridine-catalysed reaction. Values of k_b for a number of substituted pyridines are given.

Substituent	k_b	pK_a
	$l\,mol^{-1}\,sec^{-1}$	
4-methyl	6·54	6·02
3-methyl	5·65	5·68
H	3·08	5·21
4-acetyl	0·54	3·48
3-acetyl	0·41	3·18
3-chloro	0·36	2·84
4-cyano	0·095	1·90
3-cyano	0·053	1·39

Determine the Brønsted β-value for this reaction.

Using D_2O as solvent the value of k_b for pyridine is $2\cdot80\,l\,mol^{-1}\,sec^{-1}$. Does this indicate nucleophilic or general base-catalysis? Is your conclusion supported by the observations of G. L. Schwartz and W. M. Dehn [*J. Amer. Chem. Soc.*, **39**, 2444 (1917)]?

Solution. The slope of the Brønsted plot for this reaction is 0·45. This is considerably lower than for the reaction of nitrogen nucleophiles with carbonyl compounds.

(a) Nucleophilic catalysis

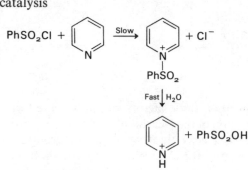

(b) General base-catalysis

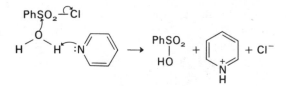

In (a) no water is involved in the slow step. Thus the low $k(H_2O)/k(D_2O)$ ratio (1·10) indicates (a) rather than (b). Schwartz and Dehn observed an unstable addition compound formed between pyridine and sulphonyl chloride in anhydrous ether, which supports the formation of the sulphonyl-pyridinium intermediate in nucleophilic catalysis. Oakenfull, Riley, and Gold report that nucleophilic catalysis is associated with less negative values of $\Delta S^{\ddagger}$ (ca. -10 e.u.) than general-base catalysis. The value reported here is consistent with this. O. Rogne, *J. Chem. Soc. (B)*, **1970**, 727.

Index of Problems

The numbers following each entry are *problem numbers* not page numbers.